How to Be a TV Quiz Show Millionaire

Publications International, Ltd.

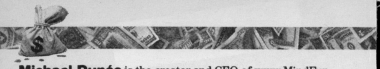

Michael Dupée is the creator and CEO of www.MindFun. com, a popular interactive trivia and brain game site on the Internet, and author of all trivia questions found in the site's "Knowledge Chamber" quiz game. He is the winner of the 1996 television quiz show *Jeopardy!*'s "Tournament of Champions." He is the fifth biggest winner in *Jeopardy!* regular season history, and is author of *How to Get on Jeopardy and Win!*. He also serves as an attorney and was former editor-in-chief of the *Florida Law Review*.

Zana Holley is V.P. of Marketing and Content for www.Mind Fun.com. She has written thousands of trivia questions for the site, including questions for the site's "Quick Quiz." The questions she writes have been syndicated and can be found on Delta Air Lines computer trivia game, in promotional ad campaigns, and in computer games developed by Gamegame.com. She is also an attorney and former research editor for the *Florida Law Review*.

Photo credits:
ABC/Shooting Star: 4, 5; **Everett Collection, Inc.:** 87, 92, 94; **Motion Picture & TV Photo Archive:** Kings World: 88; Paramount: 90; Gene Trindl: 84; **Photofest:** 6.

Louis Weber, CEO
Publications International, Ltd.
7373 North Cicero Avenue
Lincolnwood, Illinois 60712

Contents

Millionaire Frenzy!

I N NOVEMBER 1999, IRS agent John Carpenter became the first person to muster the courage—and right answers—to win $1 million on TV's hit quiz show *Who Wants to Be a Millionaire*. Carpenter said he planned to take his wife, Debbie, to Paris and feed his toy poodle, Fenway, nothing but steak. And that was his final answer.

Why has *Who Wants to Be a Millionaire* been such a smashing success?

"Simple," said host Regis Philbin. "We use the direct approach. The money doubles with every answer. As the money doubles, the questioning gets more intense, the music gets a little louder. You can almost hear a contestant's heartbeat. It knocks me out."

Philbin's charm and enthusiasm have earned millions of dollars for ABC.

Like few shows in recent years, *Who Wants to Be a Millionaire* has transcended the realm of TV to become a full-fledged cultural phenomenon. *Millionaire*'s success is a reminder that people still like to see the guy next door have a shot at winning a large sum of money on television. In this regard, *Millionaire*'s appeal is no different from that of all other quiz shows, from *The $64,000 Question* to *Jeopardy!*

Who Wants to Be a Millionaire first aired in the United States on August 16, 1999, on ABC. It ran for 13 straight nights and became the talk of the nation. The network brought the show back for a two-week run in November, and in January 2000 it put the show on its regular schedule three nights a week. On Wednesday, Janu-

Jackpot winner John Carpenter used only one "lifeline"—and that was to call his dad to say he was about to win a million bucks.

ary 12, 2000, *Millionaire* scored its highest ratings so far when 33.6 million viewers tuned in to see the show.

What sets *Who Wants to Be a Millionaire* apart from previous game shows? *Millionaire* has a sleek set. Its format is clever, and its lighting and music are futuristic. Yet, it appeals mostly as a throwback to a less cynical age. The contestants are earnest, hard-working folk, the kind of people you might work alongside every day. It's easy to pull for them as they confront the increasingly difficult set of 15 questions on the road to a cool million dollars.

"The key is the show has heart," said Michael Davies, the show's executive producer. "You're rooting for the people on the show."

Aside from Philbin, all of these elements are present in the original version of the game show, which began two years ago in Great Britain. Producer Davies is British, and his relatives told him about the British show. When Davies brought *Who Wants to Be a Millionaire* to ABC, his enthusiasm helped sell the idea to Stu Bloomberg, the chairman of ABC Entertainment. Bloomberg took a copy of the British show home and watched it.

"We had never seen a game show like this," he said. "The music, the lighting, the whole gestalt of it was perfect. The show was doing a 73 [ratings] share in England. When you hear 73 share, your ears do perk up."

A rating share is the percentage of households currently watching TV that have their sets tuned in to a particular program. Philbin said he had expected *Millionaire* to be a whopping success. "The first time I saw the show in England, I was thoroughly excited by it," he said.

Atomic energy expert Joyce Myron won the full jackpot on The $64,000 Question, *starring Hal March.*

Regis campaigned hard to be the host when Davies announced plans to move the show to American TV. It's been reported that Bob Costas and Montel Williams were the front-runners for the position, but Philbin won the job by auditioning in Great Britain. Davies quickly knew that he had found his American host: "He appears mischievous when he asks, 'Is that your final answer?' And at the same time, Regis seems to be pulling for contestants to win a million dollars."

Quiz shows have been around almost since the advent of television. In the 1950s, virtually everyone watched shows such as *The $64,000 Question.* "Back then . . . people used to have quiz show parties," said Millie Alvarez, 60, a clerk in Pasadena, California. *Twenty One* (1956–58) was hosted by Jack Barry. It was famous for its role in the quiz show scandals, with its rigged competition between Charles Van Doren and Herbert Stempel.

Jeopardy! ran from 1964 to 1975, appeared again in 1978 on NBC, and has run from 1984 to the present in syndication. Currently hosted by Alex Trebek, the show remains a favorite of America's intellectuals. *Wheel of Fortune*, a high-tech version of Hangman, has spun its wheel since 1975. Pat Sajak and Vanna White took over in '82, riding the show to phenomenal success.

In *Password* (1961–67, 1971–74), everyday contestants were paired with celebrities. The password was "success," and Allen Ludden presided graciously. In *Hollywood Squares* (1966–80, 1986–89, 1998–present), nine celebrities—stacked on a tic-tac-toe board—provide the laughs while contestants genially agree or disagree with their responses.

What has most distinguished *Who Wants to Be a Millionaire* from the 1950s quiz shows is the opportunity for contestants to get help answering questions. Contestants can confer with either the audience or friends, who can be called at home. But what really makes *Millionaire* intriguing is the money involved. With comparatively low purses, other game shows stay in the realm of innocent fun. On *Win Ben Stein's Money*, only $5,000 is in play. On *Millionaire*, the sums are of life-changing proportions.

Jealous of ABC's ratings success with *Millionaire*, the competition rushed other game shows into production. The FOX network pushed *Greed* onto the air in only one month. On *Greed*, hosted by Chuck Woolery, the payoff is $2 million. NBC brought back *Twenty One* with host Maury Povich, despite its history of fraud. CBS followed ABC to Great Britain and brought back *Winning Lines*, calling on former game show host Dick Clark to preside over the U.S. version. But will these shows be as popular as *Who Wants to Be a Millionaire*, which is simple to play, is easy for the viewer to follow, and brings on gutsy participants? "It takes a great deal of courage to actually go for the million," Davies points out. Contestants in the hot seat must choose between leaving with a tidy sum or risking it in pursuit of the ultimate $1 million prize.

But there is a fine line between courage and stupidity. Who among us would risk $500,000 for the chance to grab a cool million? If you think you want to try, check out ABC's Web site at www.abc.go.com/primetime/millionaire/mill_home.html for current details on the tryout process.

Millionaire Practice Questions

THE CONTEST TO BE ON *Who Wants to Be a Millionaire* is comprised of three rounds: the toll-free telephone qualifying round; the semifinal round, which is also played by phone; and the actual TV quiz show.

During Round One, players are asked three trivia questions. All of the questions have four answers that must be placed in the correct order. Example: "Place the following states in order going from east to west: 1. Ohio 2. Illinois 3. Utah 4. Florida." (The answer is 4-1-2-3.) Callers who correctly answer all three questions are eligible for a random drawing with all other callers who have answered all three questions correctly on that same day, and who have also selected the same tape date of *Millionaire*.

The players selected in the random drawings advance to Round Two. All semifinalists for each tape date compete against each other in a toll-free telephone playoff game that has five questions similar to the Round One questions. Semifinalists who correctly answer all five questions are ranked, based on the speed of their response. The ten highest scorers from each playoff game make the show.

Once on the show, the ten finalists compete to get into the hot seat by answering the "Fastest Finger" question. This question has four choices that must be placed in the correct order. A typical Fastest Finger question is having to put members of the musical Jackson family in order from youngest to oldest. Whoever achieves the correct order the fastest moves to the hot seat.

Winning Tip

If you Ask the Audience, put great faith in their responses. They've been right most of the time.

The contestant who makes it to the hot seat can win up to $1 million by correctly answering 15 multiple-choice questions of increasing difficulty. Each question has an assigned dollar value that increases from $100 to $1 million. A $100 question is as easy as: "Who is the President of the United States? a. Daffy Duck; b.

Big Foot; c. Queen Elizabeth; d. Bill Clinton." Suddenly, when the real money is on the line, the questions become seriously difficult, along the lines of "What is the Chinese word for applesauce?"

The contestant can stop at any time and collect the winnings he or she has already earned. If a contestant answers a question incorrectly, he or she will leave with either nothing (Questions 1 to 4), $1,000 (5 to 9), or $32,000 (10 to 15).

A contestant can use a total of three "lifelines" for assistance. The three lifelines are: "50/50" (the contestant asks the computer to eliminate two of the possible answer choices); "Ask the Audience" (the contestant asks the studio audience which answer they believe is correct); and "Phone a Friend" (the contestant may call one of up to five prearranged friends, and the friend has 30 seconds to listen to the question and select an answer).

This book includes 37 sets of questions similar to those on *Who Wants to Be a Millionaire*. Try a few sets to see if you have what it takes to win $1 million. If you do, play the telephone playoff game for a chance to get on the show. It could happen to you!

Your Quiz Show IQ

If you reach...

Level 1	You can probably also spell your name.
Level 2	You're ready for the grown-up questions.
Level 3	You're guessing at a fifth-grade level.
Level 4	Let's take the training wheels off.
Level 5	Trade that learner's permit in for a license.
Level 6	Your engine is running. Now give it some gas!
Level 7	Your competitors are starting to sweat.
Level 8	You're a frequent traveler on the information superhighway.
Level 9	Time to give Regis a call.
Level 10	You're a certified quiz whiz.
Level 11	They're expecting you at NASA tomorrow.
Level 12	Book your reservations to New York.
Level 13	You have million-dollar potential!

250 points

1 Who was the Three Little Pigs' furry nemesis?
- **a.** The Big Bad Wolf
- **b.** The Big Bad Cat
- **c.** Dr. Wolf, M.D.
- **d.** Big Bad Leroy Brown

500 points

2 In ballet, what type of shoes do the dancers wear?
- **a.** Duck boots
- **b.** Sandals
- **c.** Kulaks
- **d.** Slippers

1,000 points

3 The characters Fred and Ethel Mertz are on what classic television comedy series?
- **a.** *The Brady Bunch*
- **b.** *I Love Lucy*
- **c.** *The Jeffersons*
- **d.** *Friends*

2,000 points

4 Which of the following was fought to secure the United States' independence from Great Britain?
- **a.** Civil War
- **b.** World War I
- **c.** Revolutionary War
- **d.** World War II

4,000 points

5 Which of the following terms refers to singing with voices only, with no instrumental accompaniment?
- **a.** Forte
- **b.** Moderato
- **c.** Treble clef
- **d.** A capella

8,000 points

6 What popular TV show was the most successful spinoff from a movie ever?
- **a.** *M*A*S*H*
- **b.** *Men in Black*
- **c.** *La Femme Nikita*
- **d.** *All in the Family*

16,000 points

7 What court order, which literally means "bring forth the body," allows a prisoner to have his case reviewed?
- **a.** Petitio demando
- **b.** Writ of mandamus
- **c.** Habeas corpus
- **d.** Quid pro quo

32,000 points

8 What was the nickname of the famous fashion model who was "The Face of 1966"?

a. Twiggy **b.** Cindy
c. Cheryl **d.** Coco

64,000 points

9 In a classic poem, what is inscribed with the words, "Abandon all hope, Ye that Enter"?

a. Door to purgatory **b.** Entrance to the Garden of Eden
c. Gates of hell **d.** Kubla Khan's Pleasure-Dome

125,000 points

10 Which of the following was not a secretary of state?

a. Alexander Hamilton **b.** Henry Kissinger
c. Cyrus Vance **d.** John Hay

250,000 points

11 Who founded the American branch of the Boy Scouts?

a. Colonel Baden-Powell **b.** Herbert Hoover
c. Juliette Gordon Lowe **d.** William D. Boyce

500,000 points

12 Who was on the cover of the first *TV Guide*?

a. Art Linkletter **b.** Desi Arnaz, Jr.
c. Steve Allen **d.** Ozzie and Harriet Nelson

1,000,000 points

13 Which U.S. president appointed the first female Cabinet member?

a. Bill Clinton **b.** Lyndon Johnson
c. Franklin Roosevelt **d.** John F. Kennedy

Answers: 1. a. The Big Bad Wolf, 2. d. Slippers, 3. b. *I Love Lucy*, 4. c. Revolutionary War, 5. d. A capella, 6. a. *M*A*S*H*, 7. c. Habeas corpus, 8. a. Twiggy, 9. c. Gates of hell, 10. a. Alexander Hamilton, 11. d. William D. Boyce, 12. b. Desi Arnaz, Jr., 13. c. Franklin Roosevelt

250 points

1 What flying nocturnal mammals sleep hanging upside down?
- **a.** Cats
- **b.** Birds
- **c.** Bats
- **d.** Lizards

500 points

2 Who is the star of the popular *Pokémon* TV show?
- **a.** Poké Man
- **b.** Ash Ketchum
- **c.** Super Trainer
- **d.** Daria

1,000 points

3 What U.S. holiday was observed nationally on May 30 until 1971?
- **a.** Easter
- **b.** Valentine's Day
- **c.** Fourth of July
- **d.** Memorial Day

2,000 points

4 What does the Bible describe in Genesis 6:14 as being made of gopher wood?
- **a.** Ark of the Covenant
- **b.** Noah's Ark
- **c.** Solomon's Temple
- **d.** Baby Jesus' manger

4,000 points

5 What insurance company has used characters, such as Snoopy, from the "Peanuts" comic strip in its commercials?
- **a.** Allstate
- **b.** Progressive
- **c.** Metropolitan Life
- **d.** Auto Insurance World

8,000 points

6 What element with the symbol K is found in saltpeter?
- **a.** Krypton
- **b.** Kiridium
- **c.** Nitrogen
- **d.** Potassium

16,000 points

7 Who produced the first cars assembled completely on an assembly line in 1913?
- **a.** Henry Ford
- **b.** Karl Benz
- **c.** Rudolf Diesel
- **d.** Felix Wankel

32,000 points

8 In a famous absurdist play, who were Vladimir and Estragon "waiting for"?

a. Lefty
b. Mr. Goodbar
c. Hamlet
d. Godot

64,000 points

9 In which Bedrich Smetana opera does Marenka marry the man she loves despite her parents' schemes?

a. *Fidelio*
b. *The Bartered Bride*
c. *The Secret*
d. *La Boheme*

125,000 points

10 What percentage of states in the United States must ratify a constitutional amendment for it to become law?

a. 75%
b. 70%
c. 51%
d. 80%

250,000 points

11 Which country's King Christian IX was the grandfather of Russia's Czar Nicholas II?

a. Norway
b. Great Britain
c. Denmark
d. Germany

500,000 points

12 Who was the first host of *The Today Show*?

a. Jack Parr
b. Dave Garroway
c. Hugh Downs
d. Edward R. Murrow

1,000,000 points

13 In which movie did producers pay Sigourney Weaver $50 to perform her first credited film role?

a. *Tootsie*
b. *Ghostbusters*
c. *Mad Max*
d. *Annie Hall*

250 points
1 Why did Old Mother Hubbard go to her cupboard?
- **a.** To get a penny
- **b.** To get a dog a bone
- **c.** To see her goldfish
- **d.** To get a cupcake

500 points
2 According to myths from medieval England, what did King Arthur and his knights meet around?
- **a.** A fountain
- **b.** A square table
- **c.** A round table
- **d.** An altar

1,000 points
3 What famous waterfall is on the border between Canada and the United States?
- **a.** Niagara Falls
- **b.** Cumberland Falls
- **c.** Angel Falls
- **d.** Prices Fall

2,000 points
4 The characters Han Solo and Princess Leia are in what classic 1977 movie?
- **a.** *The Sound of Music*
- **b.** *E.T.*
- **c.** *Home Alone*
- **d.** *Star Wars*

4,000 points
5 What football team broke into *Billboard*'s Top 100 with "The Super Bowl Shuffle" in 1986?
- **a.** Pittsburgh Steelers
- **b.** New England Patriots
- **c.** Chicago Bears
- **d.** Denver Broncos

8,000 points
6 What is a trilobite?
- **a.** An ancient shellfish
- **b.** An Italian pastry
- **c.** A three-wheeled bike
- **d.** A large dinosaur

16,000 points
7 What are the articles written by James Madison and John Jay in support of the Constitution known as?
- **a.** The Declaration of Independence
- **b.** The Magna Carta
- **c.** The Federalist papers
- **d.** The Bill of Rights

32,000 points

8 What Dutch Postimpressionist painter, known for painting "Sunflowers," cut off his own ear?

a. Henri Fantin-Latour　　**b.** Vincent van Gogh
c. Paul Cézanne　　**d.** Rembrandt van Rijn

64,000 points

9 What long-running Broadway musical is based on poems by T. S. Eliot?

a. *Cats*　　**b.** *Showboat*
c. *Rent*　　**d.** *Les Misérables*

125,000 points

10 How many feet make up a mile?

a. 5,082　　**b.** 5,280
c. 5,208　　**d.** 5,820

250,000 points

11 In which Central American country do tourists visit the Mayan ruins at Tikal?

a. Peru　　**b.** Honduras
c. Mexico　　**d.** Guatemala

500,000 points

12 What statesman argued for a bimetal monetary policy in the "Cross of Gold" speech at the 1896 Democratic Convention?

a. William McKinley　　**b.** James B. Weaver
c. William Jennings Bryan　　**d.** Charles W. Fairbanks

1,000,000 points

13 What singer gave such an amazing performance of "Il Trovatore" in 1961 that she received a 42-minute standing ovation?

a. Leontyne Price　　**b.** Marian Anderson
c. Beverly Sills　　**d.** Kiri Te Kanawa

Answers: 1. b. To get a dog a bone, 2. c. A round table, 3. a. Niagara Falls, 4. d. *Star Wars,* 5. c. Chicago Bears, 6. a. An ancient shellfish, 7. c. The Federalist papers, 8. b. Vincent van Gogh, 9. a. *Cats,* 10. b. 5,280, 11. d. Guatemala, 12. c. William Jennings Bryan, 13. a. Leontyne Price

250 points
1 What is the shape of a round ball?
- **a.** Sphere
- **b.** Cube
- **c.** Cylinder
- **d.** Cone

500 points
2 What classic board game features places named for streets in Atlantic City, New Jersey, such as Boardwalk?
- **a.** Backgammon
- **b.** Monopoly
- **c.** Parcheesi
- **d.** Scrabble

1,000 points
3 Which of these is another term for the humerus?
- **a.** Thumb
- **b.** Belly button
- **c.** Wisdom tooth
- **d.** Funny bone

2,000 points
4 What classical composer went deaf but still was able to write his famous Ninth Symphony?
- **a.** Mozart
- **b.** Bach
- **c.** Brahms
- **d.** Beethoven

4,000 points
5 Which country's flag has a big red circle in the middle of a white background?
- **a.** United States
- **b.** Japan
- **c.** Egypt
- **d.** Brazil

8,000 points
6 Which of these artists lived before 1600?
- **a.** Michelangelo Buonarroti
- **b.** Edgar Degas
- **c.** Auguste Rodin
- **d.** Andy Warhol

16,000 points
7 What is the sum of a dozen, a score, and a gross?
- **a.** 176
- **b.** 177
- **c.** 256
- **d.** 156

32,000 points

8 What author created the land of Oz?

a. Robert Heinlein   **b.** L. Frank Baum

c. Mark Twain   **d.** C. S. Lewis

64,000 points

9 What German-American physicist won a Nobel Prize in 1921?

a. Darwin   **b.** Pasteur

c. Einstein   **d.** Newton

125,000 points

10 In Major League Baseball, what is the distance from the pitcher's mound to home plate?

a. 63 feet   **b.** 60 feet

c. 60 feet, 6 inches   **d.** 61 feet

250,000 points

11 In John D. MacDonald's series of "Travis McGee" mystery novels, which of the following was in each of his titles?

a. A breed of dog   **b.** A color

c. A flower   **d.** A state

500,000 points

12 What occurred on November 9, 1965, that affected 30 million people in an 80,000-square-mile area?

a. Earthquake   **b.** Power failure

c. Volcanic eruption   **d.** Nuclear meltdown

1,000,000 points

13 What is connected to the Sea of Azov by the Kerch Strait?

a. The Black Sea   **b.** The Bering Sea

c. The Baltic Sea   **d.** The North Sea

Answers: 1. a. Sphere, 2. b. Monopoly, 3. d. Funny bone, 4. d. Beethoven, 5. b. Japan, 6. a. Michelangelo Buonarroti, 7. a. 176, 8. b. L. Frank Baum, 9. c. Einstein, 10. c. 60 feet, 6 inches, 11. b. A color, 12. b. Power failure, 13. a. The Black Sea

250 points

1 What is the name of the purple Teletubby?
- **a.** Tinky Winky
- **b.** Dipsy
- **c.** Laa-Laa
- **d.** Po

500 points

2 Who was the tall, lanky schoolteacher who disappeared in "The Legend of Sleepy Hollow"?
- **a.** Washington Irving
- **b.** Julius Irving
- **c.** Ichabod Crane
- **d.** Rip Van Winkle

1,000 points

3 Which of Santa's reindeer is also the name of the Roman god of love?
- **a.** Dasher
- **b.** Vixen
- **c.** Cupid
- **d.** Blitzen

2,000 points

4 What type of instrument is a saxophone?
- **a.** Brass
- **b.** Woodwind
- **c.** Percussion
- **d.** String

4,000 points

5 What New York City jewelry store wraps gifts in a powder-blue box with a white ribbon?
- **a.** Bloomingdale's
- **b.** Saks Fifth Avenue
- **c.** Tiffany
- **d.** Macy's

8,000 points

6 What actress first guest-starred on *M*A*S*H* before going on to become a regular on *Cheers* as cerebral barmaid Diane Chambers?
- **a.** Rhea Perlman
- **b.** Loretta Swit
- **c.** Kirstie Alley
- **d.** Shelley Long

16,000 points

7 What was Ponce de Leon searching for when he explored Florida?
- **a.** The Fountain of Youth
- **b.** Kubla Khan
- **c.** El Dorado
- **d.** The Missing Link

8 32,000 points

What United States president admitted that his favorite snack was fried pork rinds with hot sauce?

a. Bill Clinton   **b.** George Bush
c. Jimmy Carter   **d.** Ronald Reagan

9 64,000 points

Which of the following was a Mexican revolutionary who fought for the rights of farmers and peasants?

a. Emiliano Zapata   **b.** Frank Zappa
c. Émile Zola   **d.** Freddie Prinze

10 125,000 points

What was the first American TV show to appear in mainland China?

a. *Dallas*   **b.** *All in the Family*
c. *M*A*S*H*   **d.** *Baywatch*

11 250,000 points

What do the children of Spain call Santa Claus?

a. Padre Navidad   **b.** Kris Kringelito
c. Papa Noel   **d.** Padre Tiempo

12 500,000 points

What was the birth name of African-American activist Malcolm X?

a. Malcolm Shabazz   **b.** Jefferson Malcolm
c. James Malcolm   **d.** Malcolm Little

13 1,000,000 points

In what exotic location were John Lennon and Yoko Ono married on March 20, 1969?

a. Tahiti   **b.** Aruba
c. Gibraltar   **d.** Mount Everest

Answers: 1. a. Tinky Winky, 2. c. Ichabod Crane, 3. c. Cupid, 4. b. Woodwind, 5. c. Tiffany, 6. d. Shelley Long, 7. a. The Fountain of Youth, 8. b. George Bush, 9. a. Emiliano Zapata, 10. d. *Baywatch*, 11. c. Papa Noel, 12. d. Malcolm Little, 13. c. Gibraltar.

250 points

1 What number should you call in most U.S. cities to reach emergency services?

a. 411   **b.** 911
c. 611   **d.** 922

500 points

2 What do you call a system of raised dots that blind people read with their fingers?

a. Telegraph   **b.** Braille
c. Print   **d.** Sign language

1,000 points

3 Which country is located at the equator?

a. Canada   **b.** South Africa
c. Ecuador   **d.** United States

2,000 points

4 What literary style requires stretching the truth a lot?

a. Folktale   **b.** Story
c. Comedy   **d.** Tall tale

4,000 points

5 If you face north and then turn 90 degrees to the right three times in a row, which way are you facing?

a. North   **b.** South
c. East   **d.** West

8,000 points

6 Professional wrestler Jesse Ventura became governor of what state?

a. Michigan   **b.** Indiana
c. Nevada   **d.** Minnesota

16,000 points

7 The Jewish holiday Passover is usually celebrated in the same month as which of the following holidays?

a. Easter   **b.** Labor Day
c. Thanksgiving   **d.** Christmas

8 — 32,000 points

Which former speaker of the House of Representatives wrote the book *Man of the House*?

a. Newt Gingrich
b. Strom Thurmond
c. Tip O'Neill
d. Trent Lott

9 — 64,000 points

Mickey Mantle hit an amazing home run in 1953. How long was it?

a. 565 feet
b. 400 feet
c. 465 feet
d. 600 feet

10 — 125,000 points

Which of the following birds is the official state bird of the most U.S. states?

a. Cardinal
b. Mockingbird
c. Western meadowlark
d. Bluebird

11 — 250,000 points

What city was a private estate before it became capital of the Philipines?

a. Manila
b. Quezon City
c. Corregidor
d. Luzon

12 — 500,000 points

Which of the following chemical elements is adjacent to silicon on the periodic table?

a. Hydrogen
b. Neon
c. Aluminum
d. Potassium

13 — 1,000,000 points

What state has the motto "Oro y plata"?

a. Nevada
b. California
c. Montana
d. New Mexico

Answers: 1. b. 911, 2. b. Braille, 3. c. Ecuador, 4. d. Tall tale, 5. d. West, 6. d. Minnesota, 7. a. Easter, 8. c. Tip O'Neill, 9. a. 565 feet, 10. a. Cardinal, 11. b. Quezon City, 12. c. Aluminum, 13. c. Montana

QUESTION SET # 7

250 points
1 In the story by E. B. White, what type of animal is Stuart Little?
a. Cat **b.** Pig
c. Mouse **d.** Spider

500 points
2 Which of the following types of ammunition is mentioned in the song, "The Star-Spangled Banner"?
a. Grenades **b.** Bullets
c. Bombs **d.** Buckshot

1,000 points
3 Where does the president of the United States live?
a. White House **b.** White Mansion
c. Presidential House **d.** First House

2,000 points
4 What is your occupation if you are a member of the bar?
a. Attorney **b.** Waiter
c. Truck driver **d.** Architect

4,000 points
5 Which video game system had kids in the early '80s glued to Space Invaders?
a. Intellivision **b.** Atari
c. Nintendo **d.** Fairchild

8,000 points
6 What pigment found in human skin helps protect us from sunburns?
a. Molecule **b.** Miasma
c. Methylene **d.** Melanin

16,000 points
7 What is the nickname of Edson Arantes do Nascimento, who many consider the greatest soccer player who ever lived?
a. Elvis **b.** Pelé
c. Kicking Fiend **d.** Peter Pan

32,000 points

8 Which humorist is known for his monologues about a fictional Minnesota town called Lake Wobegon?

a. Garrison Keillor
b. Jerry Seinfeld
c. Mark Twain
d. Tim Allen

64,000 points

9 What novel was the popular musical *Man of La Mancha* based on?

a. *Don Quixote*
b. *Cyrano de Bergerac*
c. *Faust*
d. *Gone With the Wind*

125,000 points

10 What amusement park ride did Iraqi soldiers in Kuwait take apart and send to Baghdad?

a. Ferris wheel
b. Bumper cars
c. Roller coaster
d. Tilt-o-whirl

250,000 points

11 What is the name of the former hunting lodge outside Paris where Louis XIV held court?

a. Sans Souci
b. Versailles
c. Fontainebleau
d. Habsburg

500,000 points

12 Who became an heir to the Austro-Hungarian throne after his cousin Rudolf shot himself at Mayerling in 1889?

a. Francis I
b. Franz Joseph
c. Kaiser Wilhelm I
d. Franz Ferdinand

1,000,000 points

13 Authors from what country have won the most Nobel Prizes for Literature?

a. United States
b. France
c. England
d. Germany

Answers: 1. c. Mouse, 2. c. Bombs, 3. a. White House, 4. a. Attorney, 5. b. Atari, 6. d. Melanin, 7. b. Pelé, 8. a. Garrison Keillor, 9. a. *Don Quixote*, 10. c. Roller coaster, 11. b. Versailles, 12. d. Franz Ferdinand, 13. b. France

250 points

1 What did the character Simple Simon want to taste?
- **a.** Pie
- **b.** A plum
- **c.** Tarts
- **d.** Cheese

500 points

2 If someone hugs you in the "City of Brotherly Love," where are you?
- **a.** New Orleans
- **b.** Philadelphia
- **c.** Washington, D.C.
- **d.** Chicago

1,000 points

3 According to an old saying, who is man's best friend?
- **a.** A cat
- **b.** A woman
- **c.** A dog
- **d.** A poker buddy

2,000 points

4 In what method of transportation do you pay a driver to take you in a car?
- **a.** Subway
- **b.** Taxicab
- **c.** Bus
- **d.** Airline

4,000 points

5 In the film *Air Force One*, what was the occupation of Glenn Close's character?
- **a.** Vice president
- **b.** Secretary of defense
- **c.** White House secretary
- **d.** Doctor

8,000 points

6 How long is a "score" of years?
- **a.** 4 years
- **b.** 7 years
- **c.** 20 years
- **d.** 80 years

16,000 points

7 Which warrior chief is said to have started the Iroquois Confederacy of Native Americans in the eastern United States?
- **a.** Chief Sitting Bull
- **b.** Chief Geronimo
- **c.** Chief Joseph
- **d.** Chief Hiawatha

32,000 points

8 What city had Richard J. Daley for mayor from 1955 to 1976?
- **a.** New York City
- **b.** Miami
- **c.** San Francisco
- **d.** Chicago

64,000 points

9 Which actor won Oscars for his roles in *Kramer vs. Kramer* and *Rain Man*?
- **a.** Robert Redford
- **b.** Paul Newman
- **c.** Tom Cruise
- **d.** Dustin Hoffman

125,000 points

10 How many consecutive field goals did Kevin Butler kick for the Chicago Bears?
- **a.** 3
- **b.** 80
- **c.** 24
- **d.** 13

250,000 points

11 In what country do we find the city of Karachi with five million people?
- **a.** Pakistan
- **b.** India
- **c.** Bangladesh
- **d.** Iraq

500,000 points

12 Who first flew his liquid-filled rocket in 1926 at his aunt Effie's farm in Massachusetts?
- **a.** Robert Goddard
- **b.** Wernher Von Braun
- **c.** Albert Einstein
- **d.** Ernst Mach

1,000,000 points

13 Who founded a settlement in 1819 that has developed into the island nation of Singapore?
- **a.** Lord Hastings
- **b.** Robert Clive
- **c.** Sir Stamford Raffles
- **d.** Benjamin Disraeli

Answers: 1. a. Pie, 2. b. Philadelphia, 3. c. A dog, 4. b. Taxicab, 5. a. Vice president, 6. c. 20 years, 7. d. Chief Hiawatha, 8. d. Chicago, 9. d. Dustin Hoffman, 10. c. 24, 11. a. Pakistan, 12. a. Robert Goddard, 13. c. Sir Stamford Raffles

250 points

1 Which of the following zodiac signs is also a popular model of Ford automobile?

a. Capricorn **b.** Sagittarius
c. Cancer **d.** Taurus

500 points

2 What type of animal did the pig in the movie *Babe* act like?

a. Sheep dog **b.** Elephant
c. Pony **d.** Frog

1,000 points

3 Which of these is another term for the human trachea?

a. Shoulder blade **b.** Windpipe
c. Belly button **d.** Pinky toe

2,000 points

4 Which of the following groups of animals live only in water?

a. Terrestrial **b.** Amphibious
c. Carnivorous **d.** Aquatic

4,000 points

5 What does the "A" stand for in the abbreviation for the pre-college exam, the S.A.T.?

a. Amorphous **b.** Ability
c. Agility **d.** Aptitude

8,000 points

6 What show repeats the same episode every day of the week?

a. *Blue's Clues* **b.** *Teletubbies*
c. *Rugrats* **d.** *Arthur*

16,000 points

7 Which city did Mohammed live in?

a. Mecca **b.** Jerusalem
c. Rome **d.** Cairo

32,000 points

8 Which movie director's real name is Allen Stewart Konigsberg?

a. Steven Spielberg   **b.** Martin Scorsese
c. Woody Allen   **d.** Frank Capra

64,000 points

9 What acclaimed African-American writer was a teenage minister?

a. Richard Wright   **b.** Terry McMillan
c. James Baldwin   **d.** Zora Neale Hurston

125,000 points

10 At the age of 39, who was the oldest player to win baseball's MVP award?

a. Tom "Flash" Gordon   **b.** Willie Stargell
c. George Brett   **d.** Nolan Ryan

250,000 points

11 What shape are playing cards in India?

a. Square   **b.** Round
c. Rectangular   **d.** Oval

500,000 points

12 On what TV show did married actors William Daniels and Bonnie Bartlett both win Emmys for portraying a married couple?

a. *St. Elsewhere*   **b.** *L.A. Law*
c. *Hill Street Blues*   **d.** *Falcon Crest*

1,000,000 points

13 Following Japan's disastrous earthquake in 1923, who received the message, "Hotel [Imperial] stands undamaged as monument to your genius"?

a. I. M. Pei   **b.** Louis H. Sullivan
c. Minoru Yamasaki   **d.** Frank Lloyd Wright

Answers: 1. d. *Taurus,* 2. a. *Sheep dog,* 3. b. *Windpipe,* 4. d. *Aquatic,* 5. d. *Aptitude,* 6. a. *Blue's Clues,* 7. a. *Mecca,* 8. c. *Woody Allen,* 9. c. *James Baldwin,* 10. b. *Willie Stargell,* 11. b. *Round,* 12. a. *St. Elsewhere,* 13. d. *Frank Lloyd Wright*

250 points

1 In a standard game of tennis, what piece of equipment is officially used to hit the ball?

a. Mallet   **b.** Club

c. Wicket   **d.** Racket

500 points

2 Who wanted to bake and eat Hansel and Gretel?

a. Captain Hook   **b.** The witch

c. The lion   **d.** A woodcutter

1,000 points

3 In the legend of the Pied Piper, what infested the town of Hamelin?

a. Rats   **b.** Children

c. Musicians   **d.** Roaches

2,000 points

4 What popular Louisa May Alcott novel introduced us to Meg, Jo, Beth, and Amy?

a. *Little Men*   **b.** *Little Women*

c. *The Divine Comedy*   **d.** *Pride and Prejudice*

4,000 points

5 What tire company has long been associated with sponsoring blimps to fly over sporting events?

a. Firestone   **b.** Michelin

c. Goodyear   **d.** Sears

8,000 points

6 What kind of cooking instrument is a hibachi?

a. Shredder   **b.** Pan

c. Strainer   **d.** Grill

16,000 points

7 Which artist painted a large mural, containing dozens of life-size people, on a hospital wall in Mexico City in 1953?

a. Diego Rivera   **b.** Frida Kahlo

c. Mary Cassatt   **d.** Edward Hicks

32,000 points

8 Which Mark Twain book tells of a boy's adventures on the Mississippi River?

a. *The Prince and the Pauper*
b. *A Connecticut Yankee in King Arthur's Court*
c. *The Adventures of Huckleberry Finn*
d. *The Innocents Abroad*

64,000 points

9 What kind of music did John Coltrane compose?

a. Rock
b. Reggae
c. Pop
d. Jazz

125,000 points

10 In 1985, John Howard broke a speed record riding his bike how fast?

a. 72 mph
b. 152 mph
c. 52 mph
d. 132 mph

250,000 points

11 What type of flower petals does the British royal family use for confetti?

a. Daisy
b. Mum
c. Rose
d. Iris

500,000 points

12 Who helped to found the American Philosophical Society in 1743?

a. Benjamin Franklin
b. Thomas Jefferson
c. James Madison
d. John Adams

1,000,000 points

13 In what city, on December 2, 1942, was the first controlled nuclear chain reaction created?

a. Oak Ridge, Tennessee
b. Chicago, Illinois
c. San Jose, California
d. Los Alamos, New Mexico

250 points

1 If you mix red and blue paint, what color do you get?
- **a.** Green
- **b.** Orange
- **c.** Purple
- **d.** Black

500 points

2 Which saying means that once something is done, you shouldn't worry about it?
- **a.** Two heads are better than one
- **b.** Don't cry over spilled milk
- **c.** Practice what you preach
- **d.** Eaten out of house and home

1,000 points

3 Which of the four forms of matter is water vapor?
- **a.** Gas
- **b.** Liquid
- **c.** Solid
- **d.** Plasma

2,000 points

4 In which type of literature would you find acts and scenes?
- **a.** Poetry
- **b.** Novels
- **c.** Plays
- **d.** Comic books

4,000 points

5 What living things absorb carbon dioxide and produce oxygen?
- **a.** Humans
- **b.** Fish
- **c.** Animals
- **d.** Plants

8,000 points

6 Which of the following countries stretches from Peru to the tip of South America?
- **a.** Chile
- **b.** Paraguay
- **c.** Bolivia
- **d.** Brazil

16,000 points

7 On what TV soap opera did Ricky Martin have a continuing role?
- **a.** *All My Children*
- **b.** *Days of Our Lives*
- **c.** *General Hospital*
- **d.** *Ryan's Hope*

32,000 points

8 What religion is practiced by a majority of the citizens in India?

- **a.** Islam
- **b.** Hinduism
- **c.** Buddhism
- **d.** Christianity

64,000 points

9 What opera by Puccini tells of the love of Cio-Cio-San for U.S. naval officer Pinkerton?

- **a.** *Madama Butterfly*
- **b.** *La Boheme*
- **c.** *Les Misérables*
- **d.** *Rigoletto*

125,000 points

10 Which of the following tempos is fastest?

- **a.** Largo
- **b.** Andante
- **c.** Allegro
- **d.** Allegretto

250,000 points

11 Which country besides the United States has the most active nuclear reactors?

- **a.** Russia
- **b.** France
- **c.** China
- **d.** Canada

500,000 points

12 What political party did Zachary Taylor and Millard Fillmore represent?

- **a.** Democratic
- **b.** Republican
- **c.** Free-Soil
- **d.** Whig

1,000,000 points

13 When Sherlock Holmes retired from detective work, what profession did he take up?

- **a.** Beekeeping
- **b.** Taxidermy
- **c.** Medicine
- **d.** Painting

Answers: 1. c. Purple, 2. b. Don't cry over spilled milk, 3. a. Gas, 4. c. Plays, 5. d. Plants, 6. a. Chile, 7. c. *General Hospital*, 8. b. Hinduism, 9. a. *Madama Butterfly*, 10. c. Allegro, 11. b. France, 12. d. Whig, 13. a. Beekeeping

250 points

1 Who turned the pumpkin into a coach so that Cinderella could go to the ball?
- **a.** The evil stepmother
- **b.** The fairy godmother
- **c.** The mice
- **d.** The prince

500 points

2 Which of the following drinks is mentioned in the song "Doe, a Deer"?
- **a.** Tea
- **b.** Coffee
- **c.** Coke
- **d.** Wine

1,000 points

3 In what series of TV shows and movies do Kirk, Spock, and the Klingons appear?
- **a.** James Bond
- **b.** *Frasier*
- **c.** *Columbo*
- **d.** *Star Trek*

2,000 points

4 What form of government did the Bolsheviks want in Russia?
- **a.** Monarchy
- **b.** Democratic
- **c.** Communist
- **d.** Anarchy

4,000 points

5 Which of the following hits the earth?
- **a.** Meteor
- **b.** Asteroid
- **c.** Star
- **d.** Meteorite

8,000 points

6 What is the communist movement in Cambodia called?
- **a.** Gang of Four
- **b.** Khmer Rouge
- **c.** Vietcong
- **d.** Shining Path

16,000 points

7 Which of the following words means a prominent human nose or a long, flexible snout?
- **a.** Proboscis
- **b.** Precambrian
- **c.** Hibiscus
- **d.** Minutiae

32,000 points

8 Which of the following 1970s movies was about four businessmen's canoe trip through the Appalachians, which turned into a struggle for survival?

a. *Rocky*
b. *Deliverance*
c. *Bound for Glory*
d. *One Flew Over the Cuckoo's Nest*

64,000 points

9 Which planet in our solar system has the longest day?

a. Mercury
b. Earth
c. Jupiter
d. Pluto

125,000 points

10 Who was the state of Maryland named after?

a. Marie Antoinette
b. Mary, Mother of Jesus
c. Henrietta Maria
d. Mary, Queen of Scots

250,000 points

11 Which of the following are the political subdivisions that make up Mexico?

a. Provinces
b. Departments
c. States
d. Territories

500,000 points

12 In which Shakespearean play does Falstaff die?

a. *Othello*
b. *Henry V*
c. *Henry IV*
d. *The Merry Wives of Windsor*

1,000,000 points

13 Which U.S. president was elected to the Confederate Congress after his presidency?

a. John Tyler
b. James K. Polk
c. Millard Fillmore
d. Andrew Johnson

Answers: 1. b. The fairy godmother, 2. a. Tea, 3. d. *Star Trek*, 4. c. Communist, 5. d. Meteorite, 6. b. Khmer Rouge, 7. a. Proboscis, 8. b. *Deliverance*, 9. a. Mercury, 10. c. Henrietta Maria, 11. c. States, 12. b. *Henry V*, 13. a. John Tyler

250 points
1 Which of the following is commonly worn on the feet?
- **a.** Shoes
- **b.** Shirt
- **c.** Pants
- **d.** Underwear

500 points
2 Where do we find the poem with the line: "Give me your tired, your poor"?
- **a.** The Eiffel Tower
- **b.** The Statue of Liberty
- **c.** The Great Wall of China
- **d.** The White House

1,000 points
3 What was the native language of Louis XIV and Charles de Gaulle?
- **a.** English
- **b.** German
- **c.** French
- **d.** Russian

2,000 points
4 How many pockets does a regular pool table have?
- **a.** 4
- **b.** 6
- **c.** 10
- **d.** 12

4,000 points
5 Which of the following compounds is formed by combining iron and oxygen?
- **a.** Sugar
- **b.** Salt
- **c.** Chlorophyll
- **d.** Rust

8,000 points
6 What classic TV series starred Sally Field and also featured Barbara Hershey and Richard Dreyfuss?
- **a.** *Love, American Style*
- **b.** *Gidget*
- **c.** *The Facts of Life*
- **d.** *The Flying Nun*

16,000 points
7 The widow of which of the following poets sold the rights to the epic poem *Paradise Lost* for only eight pounds?
- **a.** Dante Alighieri
- **b.** William Shakespeare
- **c.** John Milton
- **d.** Lord Byron

32,000 points

8 In what 1987 movie did Glenn Close play a spurned lover who attacks the man's family?

a. *Fatal Attraction*   **b.** *Cape Fear*
c. *Moonstruck*   **d.** *The Accused*

64,000 points

9 In what year did the Battle of Gettysburg occur?

a. 1862   **b.** 1863
c. 1864   **d.** 1865

125,000 points

10 What was the name of the first Romanov ruler of Russia?

a. Michael   **b.** Ivan
c. Nikolai   **d.** Aleksandr

250,000 points

11 In 1999, who became the first major-leaguer ever to belt two grand slams in one inning?

a. Sammy Sosa   **b.** Fernando Tatis
c. Rafael Palmeiro   **d.** Manny Ramirez

500,000 points

12 What is the more popular name of Beethoven's Piano Sonata in C# Minor, Op. 27 No. 2?

a. "Moonlight Sonata"   **b.** "Für Elise"
c. "Pathétique Sonata"   **d.** "The Well-Tempered Clavier"

1,000,000 points

13 Aside from Thomas Jefferson, what other U.S. president was born with the first name "Thomas"?

a. Calvin Coolidge   **b.** Woodrow Wilson
c. Gerald Ford   **d.** Theodore Roosevelt

250 points

1 Which of the following is usually the last car on a train?
- **a.** Engine
- **b.** Dining car
- **c.** Passenger car
- **d.** Caboose

500 points

2 Which of the following states is shaped like a rectangle?
- **a.** Colorado
- **b.** Florida
- **c.** Hawaii
- **d.** Texas

1,000 points

3 What fruit is usually used to make marmalade?
- **a.** Banana
- **b.** Orange
- **c.** Kiwi
- **d.** Persimmon

2,000 points

4 Which of the following is not a card game?
- **a.** Bridge
- **b.** Poker
- **c.** Backgammon
- **d.** Gin rummy

4,000 points

5 In the Bible, what kind of animal did Noah send out to find land?
- **a.** Dove
- **b.** Pigeon
- **c.** Bluebird
- **d.** Dog

8,000 points

6 Which of the following states is the "Buckeye State"?
- **a.** Indiana
- **b.** Ohio
- **c.** Illinois
- **d.** Florida

16,000 points

7 Which breed of dog is divided into Pembroke and Cardigan?
- **a.** Welsh Corgis
- **b.** Cocker Spaniels
- **c.** Bull Terriers
- **d.** Chihuahuas

32,000 points

8 Who was Adolf Hitler's minister of propaganda?

a. Joseph Goebbels **b.** Eva Braun
c. Adolf Eichmann **d.** Reinhard Heydrich

64,000 points

9 Which of the following words is used in New England to mean "earthworm"?

a. Shan **b.** Fishworm
c. Mosasaur **d.** Glengarry

125,000 points

10 In what modern country do we find the remains of the ancient city of Carthage?

a. Egypt **b.** Italy
c. Morocco **d.** Tunisia

250,000 points

11 Which of the following female singers has won more Grammys than any other woman?

a. Ella Fitzgerald **b.** Barbra Streisand
c. Aretha Franklin **d.** Leontyne Price

500,000 points

12 Which novel by Ernest Hemingway featured protagonist Robert Jordan?

a. *For Whom the Bell Tolls* **b.** *The Sun Also Rises*
c. *A Farewell to Arms* **d.** *The Snows of Kilimanjaro*

1,000,000 points

13 Which of these actors played a goon who was thrown off of a subway by Woody Allen in 1971's *Bananas*?

a. Zero Mostel **b.** Gene Hackman
c. Sylvester Stallone **d.** Harrison Ford

Answers: 1. d. Caboose, 2. a. Colorado, 3. b. Orange, 4. c. Backgammon, 5. a. Dove, 6. b. Ohio, 7. a. Welsh Corgis, 8. a. Joseph Goebbels, 9. b. Fishworm, 10. d. Tunisia, 11. c. Aretha Franklin, 12. a. *For Whom the Bell Tolls*, 13. c. Sylvester Stallone

250 points

1 Which of the following weather conditions is most commonly associated with winter?
- **a.** Sunny
- **b.** Snow
- **c.** Hurricane
- **d.** Clouds

500 points

2 Which of the following rivers flows through India?
- **a.** Indus River
- **b.** Mississippi River
- **c.** Nile River
- **d.** Amazon River

1,000 points

3 Who wrote "Oh! Susanna" and "Old Folks at Home"?
- **a.** Beethoven
- **b.** Mozart
- **c.** Stephen Sondheim
- **d.** Stephen Foster

2,000 points

4 What is a country's GNP?
- **a.** Gross National Parrots
- **b.** Gross National Product
- **c.** Gender Neutral People
- **d.** Great National Parks

4,000 points

5 Which of the following is not a term used in the card game bridge?
- **a.** Bid
- **b.** Trump
- **c.** Punt
- **d.** Dummy

8,000 points

6 What is a marsupium, which is found on most marsupials?
- **a.** Snout
- **b.** Tail
- **c.** Large eye
- **d.** Pouch

16,000 points

7 Who originally wrote the story of Peter Rabbit in a letter to her former governess's son?
- **a.** Anna McGregor
- **b.** Margaret Wise Brown
- **c.** Beatrix Potter
- **d.** Louisa May Alcott

32,000 points

8 Which of the following was not a member of the 1980s teen group New Edition?

a. Michael Bivins   **b.** Jordan Knight
c. Ronnie DeVoe   **d.** Bobby Brown

64,000 points

9 Which Chinese dynasty lasted from 618 to 907 and was considered the golden age of Chinese culture?

a. Ming Dynasty   **b.** Khan Dynasty
c. Manchu Dynasty   **d.** T'ang Dynasty

125,000 points

10 What was the nickname of American financier Cornelius Vanderbilt?

a. Gloria   **b.** Commodore
c. The Prince   **d.** Daddy Warbucks

250,000 points

11 Which breed of dog is the tallest?

a. Great Dane   **b.** Saint Bernard
c. Irish Wolfhound   **d.** Borzoi

500,000 points

12 After Sicily, what is the next largest island in the Mediterranean Sea?

a. Malta   **b.** Crete
c. Corsica   **d.** Sardinia

1,000,000 points

13 Where is the national headquarters of Wal-Mart located?

a. Little Rock, Arkansas   **b.** Hope, Arkansas
c. Bentonville, Arkansas   **d.** Walton City, Arkansas

250 points

1 What are French fries made from?
- **a.** Beef
- **b.** Lettuce
- **c.** Potatoes
- **d.** Tomatoes

500 points

2 What are pictures of people called?
- **a.** Portraits
- **b.** Sculptures
- **c.** Murals
- **d.** Buildings

1,000 points

3 Which president did Lyndon B. Johnson succeed?
- **a.** Abraham Lincoln
- **b.** Andrew Johnson
- **c.** Teddy Roosevelt
- **d.** John F. Kennedy

2,000 points

4 What do we call the first ten amendments to the Constitution?
- **a.** Declaration of Independence
- **b.** Bill of Rights
- **c.** Articles of Confederation
- **d.** Magna Carta

4,000 points

5 Which of the following is not a part of an atom?
- **a.** A neutron
- **b.** A magneton
- **c.** A proton
- **d.** An electron

8,000 points

6 With what country did President Nixon relax the United States' trade embargo just days after the U.S. table tennis team was invited to play there?
- **a.** Russia
- **b.** Cuba
- **c.** China
- **d.** South Africa

16,000 points

7 What athletic shoe company has a "swoosh" for its logo?
- **a.** Nike
- **b.** Adidas
- **c.** Reebok
- **d.** Converse

32,000 points

8 How many World Series did the New York Yankees win in the 20th century?

a. 12   **b.** 18
c. 14   **d.** 25

64,000 points

9 Which member of British royalty married Mark Phillips in 1973?

a. Princess Margaret   **b.** Princess Anne
c. Princess Caroline   **d.** Princess Beatrice

125,000 points

10 What Grammy-winning musical group features singer Lauryn Hill?

a. Fugees   **b.** TLC
c. En Vogue   **d.** The Cranberries

250,000 points

11 In Arthurian legend, who killed Gawain?

a. Uther Pendragon   **b.** Merlin
c. Morgan le Fay   **d.** Lancelot

500,000 points

12 What type of animals make up the second largest order of mammals, Chiroptera?

a. Bats   **b.** Marsupials
c. Shrews   **d.** Rodents

1,000,000 points

13 Which of the following singers got his or her nickname from a hearing aid retailer?

a. Sting   **b.** Brandy
c. Prince   **d.** Bono

Answers: 1. c. Potatoes, 2. a. Portraits, 3. d. John F. Kennedy, 4. b. Bill of Rights, 5. b. A magneton, 6. c. China, 7. a. Nike, 8. d. 25, 9. b. Princess Anne, 10. a. Fugees, 11. d. Lancelot, 12. a. Bats, 13. d. Bono

250 points

1 What furry animal hides colored eggs for children at Easter time?

a. Bunny   **b.** Wolf
c. Dog   **d.** Bat

500 points

2 Where were mummies laid to rest?

a. In castles   **b.** In arenas
c. In pyramids   **d.** In huts

1,000 points

3 Where are a person's biceps and triceps?

a. Eyes   **b.** Arms
c. Knees   **d.** Toes

2,000 points

4 What Disney dog has the same name as a planet in our solar system?

a. Mercury   **b.** Goofy
c. Jupiter   **d.** Pluto

4,000 points

5 Which of the following is the chemical symbol for iron?

a. Fe   **b.** Ir
c. Zn   **d.** Tn

8,000 points

6 Who was crowned king of England on Christmas Day, 1066?

a. Charlemagne   **b.** William the Conqueror
c. King Harold II   **d.** King George III

16,000 points

7 What butter company's logo features a Native American girl kneeling and holding a box of its butter?

a. Publix   **b.** Imperial
c. Land O Lakes   **d.** Parkay

32,000 points

8 Which of these geologic time periods occurred first?
- **a.** Cenozoic Era
- **b.** Jurassic Period
- **c.** Mesozoic Era
- **d.** Paleozoic Era

64,000 points

9 Who was the first U.S. president who was not from Massachusetts or Virginia?
- **a.** Andrew Jackson
- **b.** Martin Van Buren
- **b.** James Madison
- **d.** Alexander Hamilton

125,000 points

10 For whom did Elton John write his 1975 hit song "Philadelphia Freedom"?
- **a.** Ben Franklin
- **b.** Wilson Goode
- **c.** Jesse Jackson
- **d.** Billie Jean King

250,000 points

11 Which of the following newspapers has the highest circulation?
- **a.** *Boston Globe*
- **b.** *Houston Chronicle*
- **c.** *Chicago Tribune*
- **d.** *Washington Post*

500,000 points

12 In what country was Milton Obote removed from office by a coup in 1971?
- **a.** New Guinea
- **b.** Haiti
- **c.** Uganda
- **d.** Zaire

1,000,000 points

13 What state was artificial heart recipient Barney Clark from?
- **a.** New York
- **b.** Utah
- **c.** Florida
- **d.** California

250 points

1 What did Old MacDonald have?

a. A store   **b.** A factory
c. A farm   **d.** A mill

500 points

2 Which abbreviation refers to the morning?

a. A.M.   **b.** P.M.
c. B.C.   **d.** A.D.

1,000 points

3 Which of the original 13 colonies was founded by William Penn?

a. Vermont   **b.** Pennsylvania
c. Georgia   **d.** Hawaii

2,000 points

4 What German phrase do people say when someone sneezes?

a. *Guten Morgen*   **b.** *Danke schön*
c. *Auf Wiedersehen*   **d.** *Gesundheit*

4,000 points

5 What does a submersible explore?

a. Outer space   **b.** The ocean floor
c. Caves   **d.** The Himalayas

8,000 points

6 Which British romantic poet finished a draft of the autobiographical epic *The Prelude* in 1805 but kept revising it for 45 more years?

a. Robert Southey   **b.** William Shakespeare
c. Christopher Marlowe   **d.** William Wordsworth

16,000 points

7 What kid's drink has a big smiling pitcher for its mascot?

a. Hawaiian Punch   **b.** Hi-C
c. Kool-Aid   **d.** Juicy Juice

32,000 points

8 Which of the following African countries was once a colony of France?
- **a.** South Africa
- **b.** Somalia
- **c.** Algeria
- **d.** Angola

64,000 points

9 How many gold medals did Carl Lewis win in his career spanning four Olympics?
- **a.** 6
- **b.** 7
- **c.** 8
- **d.** 9

125,000 points

10 Which of the following is the real name of the singer Sting?
- **a.** Gordon Lightfoot
- **b.** Gordon Sumner
- **c.** Reginald Dwight
- **c.** Vincent Fernier

250,000 points

11 In 1981, Roger B. Smith became CEO of what American automaker?
- **a.** Chrysler
- **b.** General Motors
- **c.** Ford
- **d.** American Motors

500,000 points

12 What vegetable is credited with helping a Welsh army defeat a Saxon army?
- **a.** Broccoli
- **b.** Carrot
- **c.** Leek
- **d.** Scallion

1,000,000 points

13 Which sculpture by Michelangelo was the only one actually signed by the sculptor?
- **a.** David
- **b.** Moses
- **c.** Pieta
- **d.** Burghers of Calais

Answers: 1. c. A farm, 2. a. A.M., 3. b. Pennsylvania, 4. d. *Gesundheit*, 5. b. The ocean floor, 6. d. William Wordsworth, 7. c. Kool-Aid, 8. c. Algeria, 9. d. 9, 10. b. Gordon Sumner, 11. b. General Motors, 12. c. Leek, 13. c. Pieta

250 points

1 What did the itsy-bitsy spider climb up?
- **a.** The Empire State Building
- **b.** The Grand Canyon
- **c.** Mount Everest
- **d.** The water spout

500 points

2 What must a fish be in to breathe?
- **a.** Water
- **b.** Air
- **c.** Snow
- **d.** Soup

1,000 points

3 Which of the following genres is associated with the author Stephen King?
- **a.** Comedy
- **b.** Horror
- **c.** Humor
- **d.** Romance

2,000 points

4 During what process does the stomach make gastric juice?
- **a.** Respiration
- **b.** Circulation
- **c.** Digestion
- **d.** Evaporation

4,000 points

5 In what month is the birthday of Martin Luther King, Jr.?
- **a.** January
- **b.** April
- **c.** July
- **d.** October

8,000 points

6 What state's colleges include Burlington, Marlboro, and Green Mountain?
- **a.** Alaska
- **b.** Delaware
- **c.** Montana
- **d.** Vermont

16,000 points

7 What Emmy-award-winning actor played David Addison on the 1980s TV detective series *Moonlighting*?
- **a.** Tom Hanks
- **b.** David Duchovny
- **c.** Bruce Willis
- **d.** Kelsey Grammer

32,000 points

8 In what typical American town is the play *Main Street* set?

a. Gopher Prairie, Minnesota   **b.** Grover's Corners, New Hampshire

c. Winesburg, Ohio   **d.** Sinclair, California

64,000 points

9 Who composed the "Hungarian Rhapsodies"?

a. Frédéric Chopin   **b.** Franz Liszt

c. George Gershwin   **d.** Franz Schubert

125,000 points

10 Which of the following directors has never won an Academy Award?

a. Robert Redford   **b.** Martin Scorsese

c. Woody Allen   **d.** Sydney Pollack

250,000 points

11 Which of the following is not the title of a Danielle Steel novel?

a. *Star*   **b.** *Jewels*

c. *Five Days in Paris*   **d.** *Intruder in the Dust*

500,000 points

12 Who was the last defensive player to be Super Bowl MVP?

a. Reggie White   **b.** Chuck Howley

c. Lawrence Taylor   **d.** Richard Dent

1,000,000 points

13 What president signed the Postal Reorganization Act, creating the modern U.S. Postal Service?

a. John F. Kennedy   **b.** Lyndon Johnson

c. Richard Nixon   **d.** Franklin Roosevelt

Answers: 1. d. The water spout, 2. a. Water, 3. b. Horror, 4. c. Digestion, 5. a. January, 6. d. Vermont, 7. c. Bruce Willis, 8. a. Gopher Prairie, Minnesota, 9. b. Franz Liszt, 10. b. Martin Scorsese, 11. d. *Intruder in the Dust*, 12. d. Richard Dent, 13. c. Richard Nixon

250 points

1 Which farm animal says "moo"?
- **a.** Duck
- **b.** Sheep
- **c.** Horse
- **d.** Cow

500 points

2 What do we call the saying "Do unto others as you would have them do unto you"?
- **a.** Occam's Razor
- **b.** The Golden Rule
- **c.** Murphy's Law
- **d.** The First Commandment

1,000 points

3 What liquid food do bees get from flowers?
- **a.** Soup
- **b.** Milk
- **c.** Nectar
- **d.** Slim Fast

2,000 points

4 Which of the following terms is not used in the sport of hockey?
- **a.** Double play
- **b.** Goalie
- **c.** Puck
- **d.** Penalty box

4,000 points

5 Which of the following is not a kind of dog?
- **a.** Corgi
- **b.** Terrier
- **c.** Kiwi
- **d.** Beagle

8,000 points

6 What official at a college keeps records of the enrollment and the grades?
- **a.** President
- **b.** Registrar
- **c.** Regent
- **d.** Dean

16,000 points

7 Which popular American poet wrote "The Road Not Taken"?
- **a.** Emily Brontë
- **b.** Carl Sandburg
- **c.** Walt Whitman
- **d.** Robert Frost

32,000 points

following actors was not a regular on the NBC
Law & Order?
- **a.** Chris Noth
- **b.** Jerry Orbach
- **c.** Angie Harmon
- **d.** Daniel Benzali

64,000 points

9 How long is the current Kentucky Derby?
- **a.** One mile
- **b.** A quarter mile
- **b.** One and a half miles
- **d.** One and a quarter miles

125,000 points

10 What college was attended by roommates Tommy Lee Jones and Al Gore?
- **a.** Harvard
- **b.** Yale
- **c.** Princeton
- **d.** Columbia

250,000 points

11 In what building can you find the original engrossed Declaration of Independence?
- **a.** The Smithsonian
- **b.** U.S. Capitol
- **c.** National Archives
- **d.** Library of Congress

500,000 points

12 What painter was famous for his portrait "Madame X"?
- **a.** James Whistler
- **b.** John Singleton Copley
- **c.** John Singer Sargent
- **d.** Gilbert Stuart

1,000,000 points

13 What car company takes its name from the Japanese term for the Pleiades?
- **a.** Toyota
- **b.** Suzuki
- **c.** Mitsubishi
- **d.** Subaru

Answers: 1. d. Cow, 2. b. The Golden Rule, 3. c. Nectar, 4. a. Double play, 5. c. Kiwi, 6. b. Register, 7. d. Robert Frost, 8. d. Daniel Benzali, 9. d. One and a quarter miles, 10. a. Harvard, 11. c. National Archives, 12. c. John Singer Sargent, 13. d. Subaru

250 points

1 What would you wear if you were a figure skater?
- **a.** Roller skates
- **b.** Skis
- **c.** Ice skates
- **d.** Snowshoes

500 points

2 What did the farmer's wife use to cut off the three blind mice's tails?
- **a.** Carving knife
- **b.** Chain saw
- **c.** Machete
- **d.** Weed wacker

1,000 points

3 Which character from a classic Christmas tale says, "God bless us every one"?
- **a.** Scrooge
- **b.** Bob Cratchit
- **c.** Tiny Tim
- **d.** The Grinch

2,000 points

4 What is the name for a machine that can store, retrieve, and handle numbers according to instructions from a program?
- **a.** Abacus
- **b.** Computer
- **c.** Adding machine
- **d.** Engine

4,000 points

5 How long does it take sunlight to reach the Earth?
- **a.** 8 seconds
- **b.** 8 minutes
- **c.** 8 hours
- **d.** 8 days

8,000 points

6 What is the word *dromedary* used to describe?
- **a.** A tent
- **b.** A robe
- **c.** A bee
- **d.** A camel

16,000 points

7 From what plant is linen made?
- **a.** Cotton
- **b.** Flax
- **c.** Milkweed
- **d.** Hemp

32,000 points

8 What city is home to the Guggenheim Museum?
- **a.** New York
- **b.** Boston
- **c.** Los Angeles
- **d.** Pittsburgh

64,000 points

9 What is the maximum length of bandage that is allowed on each hand of a pro boxer?
- **a.** 18 inches
- **b.** 18 feet
- **c.** 36 feet
- **d.** 36 inches

125,000 points

10 Which of the following was *not* one of the first names of the characters in *The Mod Squad*?
- **a.** Mike
- **b.** Julie
- **c.** Linc
- **d.** Pete

250,000 points

11 What river forms the border between Zambia and Zimbabwe?
- **a.** Orange
- **b.** Nile
- **c.** Congo
- **d.** Zambezi

500,000 points

12 What Old West outlaw said "let 'er rip!" moments before being hanged?
- **a.** Cherokee Bill
- **b.** Henry Plummer
- **c.** Wild Bill Longley
- **d.** Black Jack Ketchum

1,000,000 points

13 Which of these was the best-selling book of the 1980s?
- **a.** *The Firm*
- **b.** *Clear and Present Danger*
- **c.** *It*
- **d.** *Lake Wobegon Days*

250 points

1 Which of the following do you put on an envelope?
- **a.** A stamp
- **b.** Scissors
- **c.** A key
- **d.** Spaghetti

500 points

2 What did Sleeping Beauty prick her finger on?
- **a.** Needle
- **b.** Spindle of a spinning wheel
- **c.** Pitchfork
- **d.** Serpent's tooth

1,000 points

3 Which of the following seas divides Europe from Africa?
- **a.** Caribbean Sea
- **b.** Sea of Tranquility
- **c.** Mediterranean Sea
- **d.** South China Sea

2,000 points

4 What is the special kind of wire in a lightbulb called?
- **a.** Circuit
- **b.** Switch
- **c.** Electron
- **d.** Filament

4,000 points

5 What star appears directly above the North Pole and so is used for navigation?
- **a.** Polaris
- **b.** Ursa Major
- **c.** Betelgeuse
- **d.** Sirius

8,000 points

6 What 77-year-old man returned to space in 1998, 36 years after his first flight?
- **a.** Alan Shepard
- **b.** Neil Armstrong
- **c.** John Glenn
- **d.** Buzz Aldrin

16,000 points

7 For his work on what TV show did Daniel J. Travanti win Emmy Awards in 1981 and 1982?
- **a.** *Wiseguy*
- **b.** *Mannix*
- **c.** *L.A. Law*
- **d.** *Hill Street Blues*

32,000 points

8 What naturally occurring element has the highest atomic weight?

a. Lead
b. Uranium
c. Iron
d. Silicon

64,000 points

9 Under presidential succession law, who becomes president if the president, vice president, and speaker of the House are unable to do so?

a. President pro tempore of the Senate
b. Secretary of state
c. Secretary of defense
d. Secretary of the treasury

125,000 points

10 What type of fortified wine was Amontillado, made famous in an Edgar Allan Poe short story?

a. Vermouth
b. Port
c. Sherry
d. Cointreau

250,000 points

11 In Shakespeare's *Romeo and Juliet*, who killed Mercutio, the high-spirited friend of Romeo?

a. Romeo
b. Paris
c. Friar Laurence
d. Tybalt

500,000 points

12 Which of the following islands' name refers to pelicans?

a. Alcatraz
b. Galapagos
c. Oahu
d. Tahiti

1,000,000 points

13 As a result of the 1990 census, which state lost the most seats in the House of Representatives, a total loss of three?

a. California
b. New York
c. Ohio
d. Michigan

Answers: 1. a. A stamp, **2. b.** Spindle of a spinning wheel, **3. c.** Mediterranean Sea, **4. d.** Filament, **5. a.** Polaris, **6. c.** John Glenn, **7. d.** *Hill Street Blues*, **8. b.** Uranium, **9. a.** President pro tempore of the Senate, **10. c.** Sherry, **11. d.** Tybalt, **12. a.** Alcatraz, **13. b.** New York

250 points

1 Which of the following articles of clothing is not appropriate for a cold day?

a. Wool cap   **b.** Scarf
c. Mittens   **d.** Shorts

500 points

2 In the nursery rhyme *Hey Diddle Diddle,* what did the cow jump over?

a. The cat   **b.** The fiddle
c. The moon   **d.** The dish

1,000 points

3 What is most of the earth covered with?

a. Water   **b.** Land
c. Apple pie   **d.** Ink

2,000 points

4 What do we call a scientist who studies the relationship between living things and their environment?

a. Archeologist   **b.** Ecologist
c. Psychologist   **d.** Dr. Ruth

4,000 points

5 What sport was coached by John Wooden?

a. Football   **b.** Tennis
c. Soccer   **d.** Basketball

8,000 points

6 Which of the following is the most widely spoken language?

a. Hindi   **b.** French
c. Mandarin Chinese   **d.** English

16,000 points

7 What TV news personality is married to *Doonesbury* cartoonist Garry Trudeau?

a. Katie Couric   **b.** Jane Pauley
c. Diane Sawyer   **d.** Deborah Norville

32,000 points

8 From what television show was *Empty Nest* a spin-off?

a. *The Golden Girls*   **b.** *Family Matters*

c. *Full House*   **d.** *Who's the Boss*

64,000 points

9 What was the approximate population of the world in 1850?

a. 200 million   **b.** 2 billion

c. 1 billion   **d.** 500 million

125,000 points

10 Which of the following boxers did *not* win an Olympic gold medal in boxing before winning a professional title belt?

a. Cassius Clay   **b.** Joe Frazier

c. George Foreman   **d.** Evander Holyfield

250,000 points

11 Which of the following 1990s bands took its name from a Monty Python skit?

a. Hootie & the Blowfish   **b.** Toad the Wet Sprocket

c. Sixpence None the Richer   **d.** Matchbox 20

500,000 points

12 Who, in 1985, became the first person to be called *People* magazine's "Sexiest Man Alive"?

a. George Clooney   **b.** Mel Gibson

c. Tom Cruise   **d.** Harry Hamlin

1,000,000 points

13 What is the only U.S. state that contains cities/towns beginning with each letter of the alphabet, including q, x, and z?

a. Florida   **b.** Michigan

c. Ohio   **d.** Pennsylvania

Answers: 1. d. Shorts, 2. c. The moon, 3. a. Water, 4. b. Ecologist, 5. d. Basketball, 6. c. Mandarin Chinese, 7. b. Jane Pauley, 8. a. *The Golden Girls*, 9. c. 1 billion, 10. d. Evander Holyfield, 11. b. Toad the Wet Sprocket, 12. b. Mel Gibson, 13. c. Ohio

250 points

1 Which of the following animals has the most legs?
- **a.** Millipede
- **b.** Grasshopper
- **c.** Ant
- **d.** Spider

500 points

2 Which of the following rivers is in China?
- **a.** Danube River
- **b.** Nile River
- **c.** Indus River
- **d.** Yellow River

1,000 points

3 Which of the following sluggers did *not* hit at least 60 home runs in a season?
- **a.** Sammy Sosa
- **b.** Roger Maris
- **c.** Mickey Mantle
- **d.** Babe Ruth

2,000 points

4 What is the popular name of the 1773 incident in which Bostonians dumped chests of tea into the harbor?
- **a.** Miss Spider's Tea Party
- **b.** Boston Tea Party
- **c.** Boston Massacre
- **d.** Stamp Act

4,000 points

5 Who discovered the laws of genetics?
- **a.** Albert Einstein
- **b.** Gregor Mendel
- **c.** Louis Pasteur
- **d.** Edward Jenner

8,000 points

6 What Jewish holiday is also called the "Festival of Lights"?
- **a.** Passover
- **b.** Yom Kippur
- **c.** Hanukkah
- **d.** Rosh Hashana

16,000 points

7 What rock group was led by flamboyant lead singer Freddie Mercury?
- **a.** Cream
- **b.** Kiss
- **c.** Pink Floyd
- **d.** Queen

32,000 points

8 What man was the first prime minister of independent India?
- **a.** Mohandas Gandhi
- **b.** Jawaharlal Nehru
- **c.** Rajiv Gandhi
- **d.** Robert Clive

64,000 points

9 Which of the following words describes a semicircular area at the end of a medieval church, often containing the altar?
- **a.** Entablature
- **b.** Cloister
- **c.** Campanile
- **d.** Apse

125,000 points

10 Who is the youngest performer ever to win "Album of the Year" honors at the Grammy Awards?
- **a.** Bobby Brown
- **b.** Christopher Cross
- **c.** Michael Jackson
- **d.** Alanis Morissette

250,000 points

11 What is the name of the great Moorish castle in Granada, Spain?
- **a.** El Prado
- **b.** El Escoreal
- **c.** Alhambra
- **d.** Sans Souci

500,000 points

12 What subatomic particles take their name from a passage in James Joyce's *Finnegans Wake*?
- **a.** Bosons
- **b.** Quarks
- **c.** Hadrons
- **d.** Leptons

1,000,000 points

13 What acclaimed Hollywood director created Bruce Springsteen's 1984 video for "Dancing in the Dark"?
- **a.** Martin Scorsese
- **b.** Sydney Pollack
- **c.** Francis Ford Coppola
- **d.** Brian De Palma

Answers: 1. a. Millipede, 2. d. Yellow River, 3. c. Mickey Mantle, 4. b. Boston Tea Party, 5. b. Gregor Mendel, 6. c. Hanukkah, 7. d. Queen, 8. b. Jawaharlal Nehru, 9. d. Apse, 10. d. Alanis Morissette, 11. c. Alhambra, 12. b. Quarks, 13. d. Brian De Palma

250 points

1 What kind of animal is called a chick when it is little?
- **a.** Rabbit
- **b.** Pig
- **c.** Hen
- **d.** Cat

500 points

2 How many years are in one century?
- **a.** 25
- **b.** 50
- **c.** 75
- **d.** 100

1,000 points

3 What ancient structure would reach from Maine to Florida if it were moved to the U.S.?
- **a.** Taj Mahal
- **b.** Great Wall of China
- **c.** Pyramid at Giza
- **d.** Roman Coliseum

2,000 points

4 Which of the following was a plant-eating dinosaur with horns?
- **a.** Triceratops
- **b.** Tyrannosaurus Rex
- **c.** Velociraptor
- **d.** Barney

4,000 points

5 What is the nickname shared by quarterbacks Ken Stabler and Jake Plummer?
- **a.** Ice
- **b.** Snake
- **c.** The Knife
- **d.** Money

8,000 points

6 In what city did Mary Richards live in *The Mary Tyler Moore Show*?
- **a.** New York
- **b.** Milwaukee
- **c.** Denver
- **d.** Minneapolis

16,000 points

7 What symbol appears on an Izod tennis shirt?
- **a.** Horse
- **b.** Camel
- **c.** Alligator
- **d.** Arrow

32,000 points

8 In the movie *Risky Business*, with what university's admissions officer did the character Joel have an interview?

a. Cornell
b. Harvard
c. Yale
d. Princeton

64,000 points

9 What are the chances of throwing a seven using two ordinary six-sided dice?

a. 1 in 36
b. 1 in 12
c. 1 in 6
d. 1 in 8

125,000 points

10 Which of these states was not one of the original 13 colonies?

a. Massachusetts
b. Vermont
c. Maryland
d. New Hampshire

250,000 points

11 Which novel by W. Somerset Maugham is a fictional reconstruction of the life of Paul Gauguin?

a. *The Moon and Sixpence*
b. *The Razor's Edge*
c. *Of Human Bondage*
d. *Cakes and Ale*

500,000 points

12 Which U.S. president made his home at Sagamore Hill?

a. James Monroe
b. James Madison
c. Andrew Jackson
d. Theodore Roosevelt

1,000,000 points

13 On the television series *Laverne and Shirley*, what was the name of the brewery in which they worked?

a. Schultz brewery
b. Schlitz brewery
c. Shotz brewery
d. Schapps brewery

250 points

1 Which of the following animals has black and white stripes?
- **a.** Panda
- **b.** Zebra
- **c.** Tiger
- **d.** Lion

500 points

2 What is another name for the main tune of a song?
- **a.** Harmony
- **b.** Rhythm
- **c.** Melody
- **d.** Dance

1,000 points

3 Who led the boycott of Montgomery, Alabama, buses after Rosa Parks was arrested?
- **a.** Dr. Martin Luther King, Jr.
- **b.** Spike Lee
- **c.** Denzel Washington
- **d.** Robert Kennedy

2,000 points

4 Which of the following cities is the capital of India?
- **a.** Tokyo
- **b.** Seoul
- **c.** Budapest
- **d.** New Delhi

4,000 points

5 Which of the following is not a major type of cloud?
- **a.** Corona
- **b.** Cirrus
- **c.** Cumulus
- **d.** Stratus

8,000 points

6 In a famous painting by Salvador Dali, what objects seem to be melting over branches and other things?
- **a.** Gold bars
- **b.** Ice
- **c.** Watches
- **d.** Candles

16,000 points

7 Which of these states entered the Union most recently?
- **a.** Georgia
- **b.** Florida
- **c.** Pennsylvania
- **d.** Arizona

32,000 points

8 What scientist discovered that planets move around the sun in elliptical orbits?

a. Johannes Kepler **b.** Galileo
c. Isaac Newton **d.** Tycho Brahe

64,000 points

9 What street in London is traditionally associated with fine men's apparel?

a. Cannery Row **b.** Saville Row
c. Fleet Street **d.** Houston Street

125,000 points

10 What newscaster was attacked by two strange men on the street who called him "Kenneth" and demanded, "What are the frequencies?"

a. Walter Cronkite **b.** Dan Rather
c. Tom Brokaw **d.** Peter Jennings

250,000 points

11 According to the title of a Thomas Hardy novel, who was Michael Henchard?

a. *Jude the Obscure* **b.** *Mayor of Casterbridge*
c. *The Vicar of Wakefield* **d.** *The Well-Beloved*

500,000 points

12 What was the most popular show in America from 1957 to 1960?

a. *I Love Lucy* **b.** *Gunsmoke*
c. *Laugh-in* **d.** *Marcus Welby, MD*

1,000,000 points

13 What nation's flag is the only national flag that is not square or rectangular in shape?

a. Libya **b.** Kenya
c. Nepal **d.** Cyprus

Answers: 1. b. Zebra, 2. c. Melody, 3. a. Dr. Martin Luther King, Jr., 4. d. New Delhi, 5. a. Corona, 6. c. Watches, 7. d. Arizona, 8. a. Johannes Kepler, 9. b. Saville Row, 10. b. Dan Rather, 11. b. *The Mayor of Casterbridge*, 12. b. *Gunsmoke*, 13. c. Nepal

250 points

1 Which of the following animals says "oink" and lives in a sty?

a. Fox b. Lion
c. Pig d. Kangaroo

500 points

2 How many digits are in the number 10?

a. 1 b. 2
c. 5 d. 10

1,000 points

3 What word describes an object that is the same on both sides of an imaginary line?

a. Symmetrical b. Diagonal
c. Horizontal d. Vertical

2,000 points

4 For what movie did Al Pacino win his first Academy Award for Best Actor?

a. *Sea of Love* b. *Serpico*
c. *Tootsie* d. *Scent of a Woman*

4,000 points

5 What Boston Red Sox star was known as the "Splendid Splinter"?

a. Babe Ruth b. Ted Williams
c. Joe DiMaggio d. Terry Forster

8,000 points

6 What American literary character was romantically linked to Becky Thatcher?

a. Clark Kent b. Ichabod Crane
c. Tom Sawyer d. Harry Potter

16,000 points

7 Which of the following is the traditional gift for the 25th wedding anniversary?

a. Silver b. Diamonds
c. Gold d. Pearls

32,000 points

8 What was the first song ever played on MTV?

a. "Money for Nothing" **b.** "Video Killed the Radio Star"
c. "Beat It" **d.** "Paradise by the Dashboard Lights"

64,000 points

9 How far apart are the bases on a regulation baseball field?

a. 60 feet, 6 inches **b.** 66 feet, 6 inches
c. 90 feet **d.** 45 feet

125,000 points

10 Which of the following sizes of a champagne bottle is the largest?

a. Fifth **b.** Magnum
c. Methuselah **d.** Nebuchadnezzar

250,000 points

11 In the Bible's Book of Judges, what people captured Samson after Delilah cut off his hair?

a. Samaritans **b.** Babylonians
c. Assyrians **d.** Philistines

500,000 points

12 Who was the Chief Justice of the Supreme Court when the decision in *Brown v. Board of Education* was handed down?

a. Warren Burger **b.** Earl Warren
c. William Rehnquist **d.** William O. Douglas

1,000,000 points

13 What is the name given by B. B. King to his guitar?

a. Maybelline **b.** Jezebel
c. Suzanne **d.** Lucille

Answers: 1. c. Pig, 2. b. 2, 3. a. Symmetrical, 4. d. *Scent of a Woman*, 5. b. Ted Williams, 6. c. Tom Sawyer, 7. a. Silver, 8. b. "Video Killed the Radio Star," 9. c. 90 feet, 10. d. Nebuchadnezzar, 11. d. Philistines, 12. b. Earl Warren, 13. d. Lucille

1 **250 points**

What did the three little kittens lose?
- **a.** Pajamas
- **b.** Mittens
- **c.** Pie
- **d.** Minds

2 **500 points**

What are trees whose leaves drop off called?
- **a.** Deciduous
- **b.** Evergreen
- **c.** Flowers
- **d.** Seeds

3 **1,000 points**

When you count by twos beginning with zero, what kind of numbers do you name?
- **a.** Odd numbers
- **b.** Addends
- **c.** Even numbers
- **d.** Prime numbers

4 **2,000 points**

Who played Cher's true love in the film *Moonstruck*?
- **a.** Joe Pesci
- **b.** Robert De Niro
- **c.** Sonny Bono
- **d.** Nicolas Cage

5 **4,000 points**

Which of the following terms describes lava before it reaches the surface?
- **a.** Magma
- **b.** Techtite
- **c.** Pyroclastics
- **d.** Obsidian

6 **8,000 points**

Who was the captain of the *Pequod* in the Melville novel *Moby Dick*?
- **a.** Ishmael
- **b.** Queequeg
- **c.** Ahab
- **d.** Piccard

7 **16,000 points**

What company introduced the first TV dinners to Americans?
- **a.** Hormel
- **b.** Pepperidge Farms
- **c.** Lean Cuisine
- **d.** Swanson

32,000 points

8 Which of the following actresses played a daughter of Roseanne on *Roseanne*?

a. Melissa Sue Anderson **b.** Sara Gilbert
c. Melissa Gilbert **d.** Sarah Michelle Gellar

64,000 points

9 What city is the hometown of 1996 presidential hopeful Senator Robert Dole?

a. Hope, Kansas **b.** Abilene, Kansas
c. Russell, Kansas **d.** Wallace, Kansas

125,000 points

10 Which U.S. national park contains Mt. Whitney, the highest point in the 48 contiguous states?

a. Yosemite **b.** Yellowstone
c. Sequoia **d.** Cascades

250,000 points

11 In Greek mythology, who was the beautiful woman that Zeus seduced in the form of a white bull?

a. Leda **b.** Danae
c. Europa **d.** Io

500,000 points

12 In what sea will one find the Isle of Man?

a. North Sea **b.** White Sea
c. Irish Sea **d.** Welsh Sea

1,000,000 points

13 The ashes of Grateful Dead guitarist Jerry Garcia were spread over what river?

a. Mississippi **b.** Nile
c. Amazon **d.** Ganges

Answers: 1. b. Mittens, 2. a. Deciduous, 3. c. Even numbers, 4. d. Nicolas Cage, 5. a. Magma, 6. c. Ahab, 7. d. Swanson, 8. b. Sara Gilbert, 9. c. Russell, Kansas, 10. c. Sequoia, 11. c. Europa, 12. c. Irish Sea, 13. d. Ganges

250 points

1 What comes out of a chimney?

a. Sun
b. Flowers
c. Smoke
d. Vampires

500 points

2 Which of the following words refers to the type of water that falls from clouds, such as rain, hail, sleet, and snow?

a. Precipitation
b. Evaporation
c. Condensation
d. Perspiration

1,000 points

3 If the Roman numeral I is to the left of another Roman numeral, what does it mean?

a. One more
b. One less
c. 100 more
d. 1,000 less

2,000 points

4 Which actor played Oskar Schindler in *Schindler's List*?

a. Richard Gere
b. Howard Stern
c. Bob Denver
d. Liam Neeson

4,000 points

5 Which of these units of measure is the smallest?

a. Decimeter
b. Centimeter
c. Micrometer
d. Millimeter

8,000 points

6 What, after New Year's Day, is the second holiday of the year?

a. Arbor Day
b. Martin Luther King, Jr., Day
c. Memorial Day
d. Presidents' Day

16,000 points

7 The followers of what man became known as the "red shirts"?

a. Fidel Castro
b. Ho Chi Minh
c. Giuseppe Garibaldi
d. Confucius

32,000 points

8 Which actress played the part of the ten-year-old younger daughter in the movie *Mermaids* with Cher?

a. Natalie Portman **b.** Christina Ricci
c. Kimberly Wells **d.** Katie Olsen

64,000 points

9 What country is located at the tip of the Malay Peninsula?

a. Singapore **b.** Laos
c. Hong Kong **d.** Tasmania

125,000 points

10 Which of the following celebrities was once the president of the *Harvard Lampoon*?

a. Bill Murray **b.** Tommy Lee Jones
c. Conan O'Brien **d.** Matt Damon

250,000 points

11 What King of the Franks was the father of Charlemagne?

a. Pepin the Short **b.** Charles Martel
c. Clovis **d.** Louis the Pious

500,000 points

12 What scientist gave the elements oxygen and hydrogen their names?

a. Joseph Priestly **b.** Antoine Lavoisier
c. Dmitri Mendeleev **d.** Michael Faraday

1,000,000 points

13 Which chemical element is the only element that would *not* become a gas on the surface of the sun?

a. Tungsten **b.** Gold
c. Silver **d.** Iron

Answers: 1. c. Smoke, 2. a. Precipitation, 3. b. One less, 4. d. Liam Neeson, 5. c. Micrometer, 6. b. Martin Luther King, Jr., Day, 7. c. Giuseppe Garibaldi, 8. b. Christina Ricci, 9. a. Singapore, 10. c. Conan O'Brien, 11. a. Pepin the Short, 12. b. Antoine Lavoisier, 13. a. Tungsten

250 points

1 Which tool is for tightening a screw?
- **a.** Screwdriver
- **b.** Hammer
- **c.** Saw
- **d.** Pliers

500 points

2 Who came and sat down beside Miss Muffet and frightened her away?
- **a.** A lamb
- **b.** A spider
- **c.** Old King Cole
- **d.** Georgie Porgie

1,000 points

3 How many cents is a half-dollar worth?
- **a.** 1
- **b.** 5
- **c.** 10
- **d.** 50

2,000 points

4 What sport features players using a cesta to throw a pelota over 120 miles per hour?
- **a.** Squash
- **b.** Jai alai
- **c.** Racquetball
- **d.** Skeet shooting

4,000 points

5 Which of the following is *not* a type of cat?
- **a.** Rex
- **b.** Manx
- **c.** Scottish Fold
- **d.** Saluki

8,000 points

6 Which of the following letters has the highest point total in Scrabble?
- **a.** *V*
- **b.** *Y*
- **c.** *Z*
- **d.** *W*

16,000 points

7 On what part of the body would one find the temporal bone?
- **a.** Forearm
- **b.** Pelvis
- **c.** Wrist
- **d.** Head

32,000 points

8 What author wrote *The Color Purple*?
- **a.** Alice Walker
- **b.** Toni Morrison
- **c.** Maya Angelou
- **d.** Lorraine Hansberry

64,000 points

9 Who was prime minister of England at the end of World War II?
- **a.** Clement Atlee
- **b.** Anthony Eden
- **c.** Winston Churchill
- **d.** Harold MacMillan

125,000 points

10 Founded in 1610, which is the oldest U.S. state capital?
- **a.** Boston
- **b.** Santa Fe
- **c.** Tallahassee
- **d.** Philadelphia

250,000 points

11 Who was the U.S. Attorney who prosecuted Ivan Boesky, the notorious inside trader of the 1980s?
- **a.** Kenneth Starr
- **b.** Rudolph Giuliani
- **c.** Janet Reno
- **d.** Daniel Moynihan

500,000 points

12 What Major League Baseball team is author Tom Clancy part-owner of?
- **a.** New York Mets
- **b.** New York Yankees
- **c.** Baltimore Orioles
- **d.** Cincinnati Reds

1,000,000 points

13 During the early 1970s, what then-unknown performer was Bette Midler's pianist?
- **a.** Billy Joel
- **b.** Barry Manilow
- **c.** Bruce Hornsby
- **d.** Dudley Moore

Answers: 1. a. Screwdriver, 2. b. A spider, 3. d. 50, 4. b. Jai alai, 5. d. Saluki, 6. c. Z, 7. d. Head, 8. a. Alice Walker, 9. a. Clement Atlee, 10. b. Santa Fe, 11. b. Rudolph Giuliani, 12. c. Baltimore Orioles, 13. b. Barry Manilow

250 points

1 Which of the following words comes after "Don't talk to" in a popular safety slogan?

a. The animals   b. Strangers
c. Your brother   d. Yourself

500 points

2 Which of Santa's reindeer is also the name of a person who moves rhythmically to music?

a. Comet   b. Vixen
c. Dancer   d. Blitzen

1,000 points

3 In the classic poem 'Twas the Night Before Christmas, who comes down the chimney with a bound?

a. A mouse   b. A creature
c. The children   d. St. Nicholas

2,000 points

4 In Chinese philosophy, what is the opposite of "yang"?

a. Yin   b. Yon
c. Yen   d. Yo

4,000 points

5 Over what continent did British scientists announce that they had found a hole in the ozone layer?

a. North America   b. South America
c. Europe   d. Antarctica

8,000 points

6 What country did Iraq invade on August 2, 1990?

a. Kuwait   b. Iran
c. Afghanistan   d. Israel

16,000 points

7 How many people can fit into the Chrysler that is mentioned in the B-52's song "Love Shack"?

a. About 10   b. About 20
c. About 30   d. About 40

32,000 points

8 The country of Lesotho is completely surrounded by what country?

a. South Africa   **b.** Zaire
c. Mozambique   **d.** Algeria

64,000 points

9 What South Pacific country contains North and South Island?

a. New Zealand   **b.** Indonesia
c. Philippines   **d.** Micronesia

125,000 points

10 Who was the host of the game show *Jeopardy!* before Alex Trebek?

a. Pat Sajak   **b.** Art Fleming
c. Allen Ludden   **d.** Gene Rayburn

250,000 points

11 In 1998, which Chicago Cubs pitcher tied a major-league record with 20 strikeouts in a single game?

a. Kerry Wood   **b.** Greg Maddux
c. Pedro Martinez   **d.** Mark Grace

500,000 points

12 What building is the tallest one in the United States?

a. Empire State Building   **b.** Chrysler Building
c. Sears Tower   **d.** John Hancock Building

1,000,000 points

13 What was the price on the price tag hanging from the hat of Minnie Pearl, star of *Hee Haw*?

a. 98 cents   **b.** $4.98
c. $2.98   **d.** $1.98

Answers: 1. b. Strangers, **2.** c. Dancer, **3.** d. St. Nicholas, **4.** a. Yin, **5.** d. Antarctica, **6.** a. Kuwait, **7.** b. About 20, **8.** a. South Africa, **9.** a. New Zealand, **10.** b. Art Fleming, **11.** a. Kerry Wood, **12.** c. Sears Tower, **13.** d. $1.98

250 points

1 Which of the following was the name of the main character in *Raiders of the Lost Ark*?

a. Ohio Jones   **b.** Florida Jones
c. Indiana Jones   **c.** Hawaii Jones

500 points

2 What do you call an act of betraying an ally or friend?

a. A double-cross   **b.** A double-header
c. A double-park   **d.** A double-time

1,000 points

3 In what part of the White House is the president's office?

a. North Wing   **b.** East Wing
c. South Wing   **d.** West Wing

2,000 points

4 What type of fabric is a product of certain insect larvae?

a. Polyester   **b.** Silk
c. Cotton   **d.** Wool

4,000 points

5 Who announced that he would retire "The Far Side" at the end of 1994?

a. Gary Larson   **b.** Charles Schulz
c. Matt Groening   **d.** Berkley Breathed

8,000 points

6 What talk show host's nose was broken during a 1988 episode of his show?

a. Jerry Springer   **b.** Geraldo Rivera
c. Montel Williams   **d.** Larry King

16,000 points

7 Who did Motley Crüe member Tommy Lee marry in 1986?

a. Pamela Anderson   **b.** Goldie Hawn
c. Heather Locklear   **d.** Jenny McCarthy

32,000 points

8 In the Christmas classic *The Grinch Who Stole Christmas*, what was the name of the town at the foot of the mountain?

a. Hooterville   **b.** Kindville
c. Whoville   **d.** Joyville

64,000 points

9 How many amendments have there been to the United States Constitution?

a. 10   **b.** 20
c. 26   **d.** 27

125,000 points

10 Who composed "Rhapsody in Blue"?

a. Franz Liszt   **b.** Aaron Copeland
c. George Gershwin   **d.** Phillip Glass

250,000 points

11 In what city is the movie *The Sting* set?

a. New York   **b.** Los Angeles
c. Chicago   **d.** New Orleans

500,000 points

12 Which U.S. president was the first American to win a Nobel Prize?

a. Woodrow Wilson   **b.** Theodore Roosevelt
c. Abraham Lincoln   **d.** Herbert Hoover

1,000,000 points

13 What song is played as horses are paraded before the running of the Belmont Stakes in June each year?

a. "My Old Kentucky Home"   **b.** "Pimlico Dreams"
c. "Sidewalks of New York"   **d.** "Maryland, My Maryland"

Answers: 1. c. Indiana Jones, 2. a. A double-cross, 3. d. West Wing, 4. b. Silk, 5. a. Gary Larson, 6. b. Geraldo Rivera, 7. c. Heather Locklear, 8. c. Whoville, 9. d. 27, 10. c. George Gershwin, 11. c. Chicago, 12. b. Theodore Roosevelt, 13. c. "Sidewalks of New York."

250 points

1 In the classic nursery rhyme *Hickory Dickory Dock*, what ran up the clock?

a. The mouse **b.** The sheep
c. The cow **d.** The duck

500 points

2 Which of the following trees is mentioned in the song "This Land is Your Land" by Woody Guthrie?

a. Pine **b.** Oak
c. Redwood **d.** Bamboo

1,000 points

3 According to a centuries-old saying, a rotten what spoils the whole barrel?

a. Banana **b.** Apple **c.** Papaya **d.** Kiwi

2,000 points

4 Which of the following animals uses claws to hook its prey?

a. Moose **b.** Lion
c. Porcupine **d.** Chameleon

4,000 points

5 What animals did Harvard researchers announce in 1989 could be used as a source of human transplant organs?

a. Chimpanzees **b.** Pigs
c. Cows **d.** Chickens

8,000 points

6 What talent contest TV show began in 1983?

a. *America's Funniest Home Videos* **b.** *America's Most Wanted*
c. *The Gong Show* **d.** *Star Search*

16,000 points

7 What 21-year-old became the youngest player ever to win the Masters golf tournament in 1997?

a. Pete Sampras **b.** David Duval
c. Tiger Woods **d.** Jack Nicklaus

32,000 points

8 In the TV series *Star Trek*, what was the name of the chief engineer?

a. Leonard McCoy **b.** Montgomery Scott
c. Pavel Chekov **d.** Han Sulu

64,000 points

9 For what award-winning Broadway musical was Jonathan Larson the composer?

a. *Phantom of the Opera* **b.** *The Lion King*
c. *Rent* **d.** *M Butterfly*

125,000 points

10 What insect can become a queen just by eating royal jelly?

a. Bee **b.** Ant
c. Termite **d.** King Beetle

250,000 points

11 The Bayreuth Music Festival is dedicated to the musical compositions of what man?

a. Ludwig van Beethoven **b.** Wolfgang Mozart
c. Frederic Chopin **d.** Richard Wagner

500,000 points

12 On the television show *Northern Exposure*, what was the name of the restaurant that the characters frequented?

a. The Varsity **b.** Cicely's
c. One Eyed Jacks **d.** The Brick

1,000,000 points

13 Who was on deck when Bobby Thomson hit the home run called "The Shot Heard 'Round the World" in 1951?

a. Ted Williams **b.** Duke Snider
c. Willie Mays **d.** Davey Johnson

Answers: 1. a. The mouse, 2. c. Redwood, 3. b. Apple, 4. b. Lion, 5. b. Pigs, 6. d. *Star Search*, 7. c. Tiger Woods, 8. b. Montgomery Scott, 9. c. *Rent*, 10. a. Bee, 11. d. Richard Wagner, 12. d. The Brick, 13. c. Willie Mays

250 points

1 Which of the following forms of precipitation is also a way to call out to a cabdriver?

a. Ice   **b.** Snow
c. Rain   **d.** Hail

500 points

2 The characters Lisa and Marge are on what animated TV series?

a. *Pokémon*   **b.** *The Flintstones*
c. *The Simpsons*   **d.** *Dilbert*

1,000 points

3 Which of these is another term for the human cranium?

a. Noggin   **b.** Belly button
c. Funny bone   **d.** Windpipe

2,000 points

4 If you are in "The City of Lights," where are you?

a. New Orleans   **b.** Paris
c. Rome   **d.** Chicago

4,000 points

5 Who lost the 1980 presidential election to Ronald Reagan?

a. Michael Dukakis   **b.** Jimmy Carter
c. Ross Perot   **d.** George Bush

8,000 points

6 About whose eyes did Kim Carnes sing in 1981?

a. Paul Newman   **b.** Tom Cruise
c. Elizabeth Taylor   **d.** Bette Davis

16,000 points

7 What character did Kim Basinger play in the 1989 movie *Batman*?

a. Cat Woman   **b.** Poison Ivy
c. Vicki Vale   **d.** Bat Girl

32,000 points

8 What scientist discovered penicillin in a moldy Petrie dish?

a. Alexander Fleming **b.** Jonas Salk
c. Louis Pasteur **d.** Edward Jenner

64,000 points

9 How many kings of England named Edward have there been?

a. 5 **b.** 6
c. 7 **d.** 8

125,000 points

10 What number was worn on the baseball jerseys of Hank Aaron and Willie McCovey?

a. 19 **b.** 51
c. 30 **d.** 44

250,000 points

11 In bartending, what is added to a screwdriver to make it a Harvey Wallbanger?

a. Grenadine **b.** Bitters
c. Galliano **d.** Peach schnapps

500,000 points

12 What is the southernmost world capital?

a. Buenos Aires **b.** Wellington
c. Canberra **d.** Manila

1,000,000 points

13 What larger sea is connected to the Gulf of Bothnia?

a. Black Sea **b.** Yellow Sea
c. White Sea **d.** Baltic Sea

250 points

1 At the end of *Beauty and the Beast*, what does the beast change into?

a. Parrot **b.** Carpenter
c. Prince **d.** Inventor

500 points

2 What heavenly being did John Travolta portray in *Michael*?

a. An angel **b.** God
c. Allah **d.** Zeus

1,000 points

3 In a standard game of croquet, what piece of equipment is officially used to hit the ball?

a. Wicket **b.** Foot
c. Club **d.** Mallet

2,000 points

4 Which of these medical inventions existed before 1800?

a. X ray **b.** Bifocals
c. CAT scanner **d.** Polio vaccine

4,000 points

5 What was the name of Disney's *The Love Bug*?

a. Jimmy **b.** Joey
c. Harry **d.** Herbie

8,000 points

6 According to the movie *Gremlins*, after what time should Gremlins not be fed?

a. Noon **b.** 6 P.M.
c. Midnight **d.** It's always okay to feed them

16,000 points

7 Who wrote the book *Moonwalk*?

a. John Glenn **b.** Neil Armstrong
c. Buzz Aldrin **d.** Michael Jackson

32,000 points

8 What war was the subject of *All Quiet on the Western Front*?

a. World War II
b. Korean
c. Vietnam
d. World War I

64,000 points

9 How many representatives are there in the House of Representatives?

a. 356
b. 435
c. 236
d. 582

125,000 points

10 How many time zones are there covering the 50 United States?

a. 4
b. 5
c. 6
d. 7

250,000 points

11 What do we call the food that the Germans call *Kartoffel*?

a. Cabbage
b. Carrot
c. Potato
d. Celery

500,000 points

12 What is the tallest national monument in the United States?

a. Statue of Liberty
b. Gateway Arch
c. Washington Monument
d. Jefferson Memorial

1,000,000 points

13 In what human organ would you find the islets of Langerhans?

a. Skin
b. Brain
c. Kidney
d. Pancreas

Answers: 1. c. Prince, 2. a. An angel, 3. d. Mallet, 4. b. Bifocals, 5. d. Herbie, 6. c. Midnight, 7. d. Michael Jackson, 8. d. World War I, 9. b. 435, 10. c. 6, 11. c. Potato, 12. b. Gateway Arch, 13. d. Pancreas

250 points

1 Which of the following characters from *Toy Story* says, "To infinity and beyond!"

a. Rex   **b.** Woody
c. Buzz Lightyear   **d.** Mr. Potato Head

500 points

2 What mythical animal is named for the single horn that grows from its forehead?

a. Oryx   **b.** Unicorn
c. Rhinoceros   **d.** Goat

1,000 points

3 What country did Quasimodo, the hunchback, live in?

a. Australia   **b.** Britain
c. Canada   **d.** France

2,000 points

4 How many days does a leap year have?

a. 365   **b.** 366
c. 345   **d.** 346

4,000 points

5 What type of dogs did Cruella DeVille want to make a fur coat out of?

a. Dalmatians   **b.** Beagles
c. Chihuahuas   **d.** Great Danes

8,000 points

6 Tuskegee National Forest lies just east of Montgomery in what state?

a. Alabama   **b.** Mississippi
c. Georgia   **d.** Louisiana

16,000 points

7 In the film *Big*, on what machine did character Josh Baskin make a wish to become big?

a. Wishing Well   **b.** Cosmic 8 Ball
c. Zoltar   **d.** Madame Esmeralda

32,000 points

8 What Broadway musical is based on the Shakespearean play *Taming of the Shrew*?

a. *Kiss Me Kate* **b.** *Rent*
c. *Hello, Dolly* **d.** *Cats*

64,000 points

9 On TV's *Magnum, P.I.*, what was the name of Magnum's unseen boss?

a. Bruce Higgins **b.** Charles Townsend
c. Robin Masters **d.** Steven Young

125,000 points

10 Who signed the U.S. Constitution on behalf of the state of New York?

a. James Madison **b.** Roger Sherman
c. James McHenry **d.** Alexander Hamilton

250,000 points

11 To what type of bird was Percy Shelley speaking when he wrote, "Hail to thee blithe Spirit"?

a. Hummingbird **b.** Skylark
c. Nightingale **d.** Eagle

500,000 points

12 What ancient hero "untied" the Gordian knot?

a. Hercules **b.** Xerxes
c. King Arthur **d.** Alexander the Great

1,000,000 points

13 What trusted TV actor is the long-time husband of beach movie star Shelley Fabares?

a. Ed Asner **b.** Mike Farrell
c. Kelsey Grammer **d.** Carroll O'Connor

Answers: 1. c. Buzz Lightyear, 2. b. Unicorn, 3. d. France, 4. b. 366, 5. a. Dalmatians, 6. a. Alabama, 7. c. Zoltar, 8. a. *Kiss Me Kate*, 9. c. Robin Masters, 10. d. Alexander Hamilton, 11. b. Skylark, 12. d. Alexander the Great, 13. b. Mike Farrell

250 points

1 Who is Mickey Mouse's girlfriend?

a. Daisy Duck   b. Babs Bunny
c. Minnie Mouse   d. Dot Warner

500 points

2 How many senses do people have?

a. Three   b. Five
c. Seven   d. Nine

1,000 points

3 In which sport did the 1996 U.S. Olympic team earn gold medals and the nickname "The Magnificent Seven"?

a. Figure skating   b. Soccer
c. Basketball   d. Gymnastics

2,000 points

4 Which of the following countries is known for its coffee production?

a. China   b. Columbia
c. Canada   d. Chile

4,000 points

5 What writer wrote the No. 1 best-selling novel *Firestarter*?

a. Stephen King   b. Danielle Steele
c. Tom Clancy   d. John Grisham

8,000 points

6 What TV police drama starred Johnny Depp?

a. *Hill Street Blues*   b. *21 Jump Street*
c. *Airwolf*   d. *Miami Vice*

16,000 points

7 Who was Michael Dukakis's running mate in the 1988 presidential election?

a. James Stockdale   b. Evander Holyfield
c. Lloyd Bentsen   d. Dan Quayle

32,000 points

8 Which of the following teams of writers and artists created Superman?

a. Jerry Siegel and Joe Shuster **b.** Alan Moore and Rob Liefeld

c. Stan Lee and Jack Kirby **d.** Bob Kane and Bill Finger

64,000 points

9 Who holds the record of having a *Billboard* Top 40 hit every year for 29 consecutive years?

a. The Beatles **b.** Elton John

c. Eric Clapton **d.** Elvis Presley

125,000 points

10 Which European country contains the mouth of the Tagus River?

a. Italy **b.** Romania

c. Portugal **d.** Lithuania

250,000 points

11 The *Analects* are a collection of sayings attributed to what man?

a. The Buddha **b.** Plato

c. Aristotle **d.** Confucius

500,000 points

12 Which of these subatomic particles has the least mass?

a. Electron **b.** Neutron

c. Proton **d.** Meson

1,000,000 points

13 What is the English translation of the title of the Johann Strauss opera *Die Fledermaus*?

a. The Mouse River **b.** The Bat

c. The Feather **d.** The Chatterbug

Answers: 1. c. Minnie Mouse, **2.** b. Five, **3.** d. Gymnastics, **4.** b. Columbia, **5.** a. Stephen King, **6.** b. *21 Jump Street*, **7.** c. Lloyd Bentsen, **8.** a. Jerry Siegel and Joe Shuster, **9.** b. Elton John, **10.** c. Portugal, **11.** d. Confucius, **12.** a. Electron, **13.** b. The Bat

Greed

HOST CHUCK WOOLERY ASKS THE PIVOTAL QUESTION: "You wanna keep the cash or do you feel the need for greed?" *Greed* is a very cool game. Produced by Dick Clark on the FOX network, the show gets to the big money fast via an eight-tier "Tower of Greed" that starts at $25,000 and peaks at $2 million. The questions are relatively easy at first, but not as simple as *Millionaire*'s

Woolery offers $2 million.

$100 level. Instead of a mere $100, the five team members on *Greed* are going for $5,000 apiece from the get-go. Mr. Woolery, whose last big gig was *Love Connection*, happily drew this distinction. "On *Greed*, we start off with serious money," he said. "We're not foolin' around here."

This is how the game is played: One contestant, out of six, quickly is eliminated with an opening "qualifying question." Here's a sample qualifier: "How many hours does the average woman cry in a lifetime?" The answer is 476 hours. The five contestants who punch in answers closest to 476 hours survive to start winning money. The person closest to the correct answer gets to be captain. He or she then keeps determining whether the team will cash in or keep playing.

The first question is worth $25,000. The questions at this level are similar to the following:

What city is headquarters for both CNN and Coca-Cola?

a. Chicago   **b.** Miami   **c.** Detroit   **d.** Atlanta

A team member picks an answer, and then the captain either accepts or overrules it. If you chose Atlanta, you were right. The captain can then choose to keep the money or risk it for more. The FOX "attitude" kicks in after $100,000 has been won. It's time for Mr. Woolery to gleefully "activate the Terminator." Unable to afford Arnold Schwarzenegger, *Greed* settles for flashing lights that eventually shine on one of the players. It's time for that contestant to make a cutthroat choice: Keep the team in place or "call out" one of its members for a one-on-one, single-question face-off. The instigator gets $10,000 no matter what happens. The vanquished forfeits all winnings. Example of a question asked in a face-off: How many crayons are in a basic Crayola box? The answer is 8.

Winning Tip

If the "Terminator" lands on you the first time it is used, you should definitely challenge someone. The $10,000 that you will be guaranteed at that moment is worth risking the nonguaranteed money you have accumulated.

Woolery also has other enticements to offer—such as when a surviving three-member team decided to go for a half-million bucks. The host sidled up to team captain Sandy with 50 grand in cash. The team could split it three ways and go home or risk everything for a chance to divide ten times as much. The following is an example of a question the team would have to answer if it chose to continue:

Of the following items, which four were introduced to America first?

a. MTV   **b.** Compact disc   **c.** Big Mac
d. *Saturday Night Live*   **e.** *Ms.* magazine   **f.** The Energizer
g. Cabbage Patch Kids   bunny

The right answer is Big Mac, *Ms.* magazine, *Saturday Night Live*, and MTV.

The team continues to decide whether to stop or go for up to $2 million. By this point, *Greed* gets pretty pulsating. And entertaining. And even surprisingly educational.

Get on the Show

If you'd like to be a contestant, call 1-900-407-7777 and listen for further instructions. It'll cost you $1.99. You'll have to give them your name, date of birth, and a phone number where you can be reached from 1 to 6 P.M.

Hollywood Squares

THE CURRENT HOLLYWOOD SQUARES PREMIERED in the fall of 1998. It is based on the classic TV game show by the same name that began in 1966 and lasted for 14 years. On the original *Hollywood Squares*, Peter Marshall played host to such personalities as Rose Marie, Wally Cox, and Paul Lynde. The corny charm of the original—with its $1.50 daytime-TV look and its gang of has-been celebrities—is absent in the newer, slicker version.

This isn't the first new version of the old favorite. John Davidson was host of a *Hollywood Squares* that lasted for three seasons in the late 1980s. Comic Joan Rivers and disc jockey/actor Shadoe Stevens occupied the center square.

With the new *Hollywood Squares* having snared Whoopi Goldberg as executive producer and center square, the show has become a big hit. Comedians Roseanne, Robin Williams, and Billy Crystal have yucked it up in the hallowed cubes. That's not all. Cindy Crawford and Garth Brooks also made their game show debuts on the *Hollywood Squares*.

"Whoopi has given the show a recognition factor," said Susan Abramson, the coordinating producer for *Hollywood Squares*. "It's certainly easier to attract high-profile guests to the show thanks to Whoopi. People come to her like bees to honey." "Whoopi is like a magnet for this show," echoed *Hollywood Squares* host Tom Bergeron, formerly on ABC's *Good Morning America*.

Winning Tip

The celebrities are sometimes fed humorous material by the show's writers. According to informal statistics, a celebrity is 50 percent less likely to be bluffing if he or she makes a joke first.

Whoopi signed a multiyear deal to produce and appear in the game show, which is on TV in syndication five days a week. The show is scripted by comedy writers. "We want to make it a big party that is slightly politically incorrect," Goldberg said in New Orleans during a convention of television syndicate executives.

The game is played like this: It is basically a big tic-tac-toe board filled with celebrities. Two contestants play against each other. One plays the *X*s; the other plays the *O*s. When it is a contestant's turn, he or she chooses a square to fill. A trivia question is posed by host Bergeron ("What's the happiest

Jerry Mathers played another "square."

place on earth?"). That triggers a jokey comeback from the occupant of the chosen square ("It's the proving ground for Viagra"). Then, when the swells of laughter subside, the celebrity will tender the official answer ("Disneyland"). But is this the right or wrong answer? Contestant *X* or *O* must correctly judge if the celebrity's answer is right to claim that square.

Games start with $1,000 for the first two rounds, $2,000 for Round Three, and $4,000 for Round Four and every round thereafter. Whoever has the most money at the end of the rounds is declared the champion and plays for a bonus prize, such as a car or a trip.

Get on the Show

If you are in the Los Angeles area or plan on visiting L.A., you can call the Hollywood Squares Contestant Department to set up an interview. If you are from out of town and are invited in for a studio day, you must understand that any travel or hotel accommodations would be at your own expense. To set up a contestant interview, call (323) 850-0707 Monday through Friday from 10:00 A.M. to 5:00 P.M. (Pacific time). This interview will take approximately 1½ hours.

For audience ticket information, call CBS Audience Department at (323) 575-2458. For a group of 15 or more, call (323) 575-2448.

Jeopardy!

*J*EOPARDY! WAS INVENTED BY MERV GRIFFIN. It was Merv's wife, Julianne, who suggested that the show give the answers and make the contestants come up with the questions. She was making a joking reference to the game show scandals of the 1950s in which contestants were given the "answers." Merv also composed the famous *Jeopardy!* theme music himself.

Is Alex smarter than his guests?

The current incarnation of *Jeopardy!* has enjoyed a 15-year run of success, but it started out originally on NBC, hosted by Art Fleming. The current host is Alex Trebek, of course. Rumor has it that Trebek once took and passed the very difficult *Jeopardy!* qualifying test.

The game consists of three contestants who choose from six categories of five questions each (ranging from $100 to $500 and then, in "Double Jeopardy," $200 to $1,000). Typical category: "World Leaders." Alex says, "This British leader offered peace in our time." Whoever is the first to answer "Who is Neville Chamberlain?" wins the value of the question. In the "Daily Double" and "Final Jeopardy," contestants can gamble on doubling—or losing—large chunks of their earnings.

It is theoretically possible to win $283,200 in a single *Jeopardy!* game. The contestant who won the most money in a single five-game stint on *Jeopardy!* was a New York transit cop named Frank Spangenberg. He amassed over $102,000 in five games.

Winning Tip

If you get a "Daily Double" near the end of the game, and you are already leading, bet enough so that you have one dollar more than double your opponent's score.

Get on the Show

In Los Angeles, qualifying tests are conducted in the studio several times a month, and you can set up an appointment. For information on how to schedule a testing appointment, write to:

Jeopardy! Contestants
Sony Picture Studios
10202 West Washington Blvd.
Culver City, CA 90232
Or call (310) 244-5367

Do not go to L.A. just to take the test. The chance of making it as a contestant is not worth the expense. But if you are out there anyway, go for it. You can also register on the *Jeopardy!* Web page: www.spe.sony.com/tv/shows/jeopardy.

Another place to take the qualifying test is in Atlantic City, New Jersey. For two weeks a year, usually around February, *Jeopardy!* runs ongoing tryouts at Merv Griffin's Resort Hotel Casino. Since thousands of people try out, there is a two-step process. You first take a ten-question test. If you get at least eight right, you'll be called back to take the infamous 50-question preliminary test. The 50-question test is composed of $1,000-level questions from the show. You have to get at least 35 questions right to have a shot at being picked as a contestant for the show.

Also, every year *Jeopardy!* travels around the country holding contestant searches in various cities, including Seattle, Dallas, Houston, Atlanta, Boston, Baltimore, Cleveland, and Sacramento. Most of the contestant searches have occurred in April, May, and June. If you live near any of these cities, make sure to watch the show every day in the spring to look for announcements regarding the local contestant searches.

Successful test-takers are invited to play a mock version of the game. If that goes well, they may be called to be scheduled as contestants, from one month up to one year after the tryout.

Twenty One

NBC JOINED the game show craze by bringing back its 1950s hit. *Twenty One* entered TV's hall of infamy when America learned that the competition was rigged. Hoping that the new, honest version will provide ratings like those for *Who Wants to Be a Millionaire*, NBC hired talk show veteran Maury Povich as host and started airing hour-long episodes in January 2000. The network plans to continue the show if the ratings are strong.

Povich watched the original as a kid.

The first *Twenty One*, hosted by Jack Barry, ran for two years in the 1950s. After the show had left the air amid frequent rumors that TV quiz shows were rigged, a former *Twenty One* winner, Charles Van Doren, admitted that he had been fed the questions in advance. Van Doren, a Columbia University instructor, enjoyed an 11-week run on *Twenty One* after beating reigning champ Herbert Stempel. *Quiz Show*, the 1994 movie directed by Robert Redford, was based on the scandal.

The new *Twenty One* has moved around the NBC schedule, looking for a place to land. If the quiz show becomes a regular series, it's likely that at least one of the five weekly *Dateline NBC* installments could be replaced.

As in the original version, the new *Twenty One* pits two contestants against each other in soundproof isolation booths. They race to see who can be the first to earn 21 points by answering various questions. NBC had hoped to air the new version live, but technical problems prevented that in time for January. It is possible that NBC may decide to switch to a live format in the future.

Unlike the original show, contestants have no prize limit. Theoretically, players can win millions of dollars up until the point they're beaten by a challenger. Players snag $10,000 for each point they score, up to $210,000 per game. Their final winnings for each game are based on their own score minus the score of their opponent. To

make things more interesting, the new version also includes multiple-choice questions, a lightning round, and audience participation tie-in through the Internet. The show tapes in NBC's Burbank studios and features music provided by a live orchestra.

Povich said he has a fond feeling for both NBC and *Twenty One*. The original, he said, "was a show I remember watching when I was growing up." He said he was disappointed when the show was tainted by scandal. "It had a certain intellectual drama about it," he said.

Winning Tip

When you reach the second round, you will have the chance to take the money you have won and go home. Remember, your final winnings from previous shows will be reduced by the amount your challenger has if you depart, so take that into account.

Povich said he was excited by not just *Twenty One* but the whole game show revival. The genre, he said, "is wholesome and yet offers [viewers] a whole sense of drama." He's not worried about too many game shows flooding the market. "Like anything else in television, it'll work until it doesn't work anymore," he said.

Wheel of Fortune

THE LONG-RUNNING *WHEEL OF FORTUNE* is hosted by Pat Sajak and the very popular Vanna White. A former cheerleader, White is listed in *The Guinness Book of World Records* as the person who has clapped the most times on television—over two million times!

Pat Sajak loves hosting the show. "We tape five shows an evening," he explained. "I'll tape two or three days in a row. We only tape 39 days a year...so it's hard to get burned out. In many ways, it's the dream job of show business.... My kids hardly know I have a job."

When asked the secret behind *Wheel of Fortune*'s extraordinary run of success, Sajak said: "I'm assuming it's me. It can't be that goofy wheel. No, for some reason we have struck a chord. Somewhere along the line, we became part of the popular culture. People like the game. It's 30 minutes during the day when most of the family can agree on something to watch."

The game play on *Wheel of Fortune* begins with lighted squares being revealed. These squares stand for letters in the word or

Sajak adores his job—especially since he works just 39 days a year.

group of words the contestants must guess to solve the puzzle. The object of the game is very similar to Hangman, except instead of trying to guess the word(s) before a man is hung, the contestants are trying to guess before the wheel takes away their turn with "Bankrupt!"

The wheel, comprised mostly of dollar figures, is spun. All three contestants clap. If a contestant guesses a letter that's not on the board, he or she loses the turn to the next player. If the next player requests consecutive letters that are on the board—and solves the puzzle—he or she wins the accumulated money from all of his or her spins. The contestant who solves the puzzle gets to keep the amount of money he or she has earned from spinning the wheel during that puzzle. So, in this show, the losers can take home cash, not just "parting gifts," if they have solved a puzzle—a nice touch.

After four or five puzzles are played, depending on the time, the contestant who has won the most money gets to play a bonus round for big prizes, like a new vehicle or $25,000.

Winning Tip

On *Wheel*, the free letters they give you at the start of the bonus game—*R, S, T, L, N,* and *E*—are also the best ones to pick during the regular game.

Get on the Show

Send a postcard with your name, address, and phone number—and dates you'll be in Los Angeles—to:

Wheel of Fortune
10202 W. Washington Blvd.,
Suite 5300
Culver City, CA 90232

Candidates whose postcards are randomly selected will be given auditions. Auditions are held throughout the year, both in L.A. and during contestant searches around the U.S. Auditions involve a fill-in-the-blank test and a mock game.

The most up-to-date information on auditions is available by calling (213) 520-5555, Monday through Friday, from 10:00 A.M. to 6:00 P.M. (Pacific time). For information on attending the show as an audience member, call 1-800-482-9840.

Win Ben Stein's Money

WIN *BEN STEIN'S MONEY* is one of Comedy Central's biggest hits. Just look at how many times it was airing in late 1999: 3:30, 7:30, and 11:30 P.M. weekdays, and 10:00 and 10:30 A.M. Saturdays. Ben's droll humor and deadpan delivery of tricky trivia questions won the cable show two Emmy Awards in 1999—for outstanding writing in a game show and Game Show of the Year. Ben Stein is a former speechwriter for Richard Nixon and a professor of law at Pepperdine University, as well as an actor. In other words, he's as smart as he looks.

Stein is dead serious about his money.

In *Win Ben Stein's Money*, Ben is pitted against three contestants in each episode of the show. The hook is that the prize money—which can go as high as $5,000 per show—belongs to Ben Stein, so the more contestants win, the less he gets paid as host for each episode. When there is a particularly smart contestant, it's a lot of fun to watch.

Ben's tongue-in-cheek air of superiority is oddly charming. "Today I'm putting $5,000 of my money on the line," Ben intones as the game begins. "Why have I done it? Call me crazy; also call me fairly sure that [the contestants] don't have a chance against me." Sidekick Jimmy Kimmel also provides comic relief while functioning as the show's announcer.

Win Ben Stein's Money is made up of three rounds. In the first round, three contestants compete against each other. In the second round, the two contestants with the highest scores battle Stein himself. And in the final round, Ben and the highest-scoring contestant compete for the balance of Ben's $5,000 by answering a series of ten questions. Ben and his opponent take turns waiting in isolation booths (reminiscent of *Twenty One*). Ben's booth is elaborately furnished while the contestant's booth looks ready for condemnation.

Winning Tip

The key to *Win Ben Stein's Money* is the buzzer. Rather than one lone push, you need to keep pushing "rapid fire."

Win Ben Stein's Money is a smart quiz show. The questions are *Jeopardy!* caliber—or higher. The show has intellectual puns for categories, such as "Don't Put Descarte Before the Horse" and "There's a Right Way and a Hemingway."

The questions tend to cover traditional academic areas of knowledge, such as, "What is a baby kangaroo called? A Joey." And: "Amerigo Vespucci reported finding the mouth of the Rio de la Plata, which forms the border between which two South American countries? Argentina and Uruguay." Due to the level of difficulty, viewers who play at home may find themselves adding an unnecessary "What is . . ." to the beginning of their answers (a la *Jeopardy!*).

Get on the Show

If you would like a chance to win Ben Stein's money, call the show (based in Los Angeles) at (213) 520-4236, or send them an e-mail at futility@futility.com with your name, address, and evening phone. If you would like to be part of the audience, call (818) 998-8195. For further information, visit Comedy Central's website: www.comedycentral.com.

Winning Lines

L ike Regis Philbin, CBS host Dick Clark is trying to give away $1 million to a contestant—and 50 grand to you at home! *Winning Lines* starts out with 49 contestants, who are all assigned numbers. The contestants answer general questions that have numerical answers. Most of these 49 contestants are quickly eliminated, leaving six contestants who must continue to answer questions.

In the next round, "Sudden Death," the answers to the questions are one of the contestant's numbers. Example: If you add 6 to the number of Beatles, what would you get? Answer: 10—which would also be the number of one of the contestants. If the answer to the question is a contestant's own number, and he or she is not the first to ring in, then that contestant is eliminated. Also, if a contestant rings in with the wrong answer, he or she is eliminated.

Winning Tip

In "Wonderwall," you're allowed to pass on two questions, miss two, and stop the clock for 15 seconds twice. Thus, you should go fast and not worry about being right until you have used up the six freebies.

The game culminates in the "Wonderwall," with the one last finalist in a three-minute race against the clock to answer 20 questions with the answers displayed randomly across three giant projection screens. The reward: $1 million. Luckily, the finalist has a "Bail Out" button. If the contestant whacks it before the three-minute timer runs out, he or she can keep the money won up until that point.

Get on the Show

Winning Lines uses quizzes and interviews to choose contestants. Dial 1-800-264-7979 and follow the directions.

So that you at home won't feel left out, Clark reveals a seven-digit home-game number. If your phone number (after the area code) has all seven digits in any order, you might win $50,000!